1812–1883.

MARTHA

OR

THE FAIR AT RICHMOND

A Comic Romantic Opera
in Four Acts

Libretto by

W. FRIEDRICH

Music by

FRIEDRICH VON FLOTOW

The English Version by
NATALIA MACFARREN

With an Essay on the
Story of the Opera by
H. E. KREHBIEL

G. SCHIRMER, Inc., NEW YORK

MARTHA

Characters of the Drama

LADY HARRIET DURHAM, Maid-of-honor to Queen Anne	Soprano
NANCY, her friend	Mezzo-Soprano
SIR TRISTRAM MICKLEFORD, Lady Harriet's cousin .	Bass
LIONEL	Tenor
PLUNKETT, a wealthy farmer	Bass
THE SHERIFF OF RICHMOND	Bass
THREE SERVANTS OF LADY HARRIET . . .	Tenor and Two Basses
THREE MAIDSERVANTS	Soprano and Mezzo-Soprano

Chorus of Ladies, Servants, Farmers, Hunters and Huntresses, Pages, &c.

THE SCENE IS LAID, AT FIRST, IN THE CASTLE OF LADY HARRIET, THEN IN RICHMOND AND ENVIRONS, DURING THE REIGN OF QUEEN ANNE

MARTHA

OR

THE FAIR AT RICHMOND

A SEMI-SERIOUS OPERA IN FOUR ACTS

Words by W. FRIEDRICH (F. W. RIESE)

Music by

FRIEDRICH FREIHERR VON FLOTOW

First Performed at the Court Opera, Vienna, on November 25th, 1847, with the Following Cast:

LADY HARRIET, ...	Soprano, . . .	ANNA ZERR
NANCY, ...	Contralto, . . .	THERESE SCHWARZ
LIONEL, ...	Tenor, ...	JOSEPH ERL
PLUNKETT, ...	Bass, ...	CARL FORMES

Martha.

The history of Flotow's "Martha," the "ever popular," as it has come to be called in England, is full of incident, but does not appear ever to have been correctly set down in all its details. The hand-books disagree hopelessly as to titles, dates and performers. Who sang the rôle of *Lionel* at the first performance of the opera in Vienna? The lexicons say Herr Ander; the widow of the composer, who wrote his biography ten years after his death, says Erl. The latter was a popular singer at the Court Opera in 1847, at the zenith of his career and the height of his powers; the former was still a novice on the stage and ten years Erl's junior. I have, therefore, accepted the statement of the widow of the composer, although she did not become his wife until twenty-one years after the original production of the opera and may not have written from original information. Who sang the part of *Nancy* when the opera was given for the first time in its Italian garb in Paris? The "Dictionnaire des Opéras," by Clément and Larousse, says it was Madame Nantier-Didiée; Flotow's biographer says it was Marietta Alboni. One book gives the title of the French ballet which provided Flotow with his story as "Lady Henriette, ou la Foire de Richmond"; another as "Lady Harriette, ou la Servante de Greenwich." So among the German titles of the opera we find "Martha, oder der Markt zu Richmond," and also "Martha, oder der Mägdemarkt zu Richmond"; yet "Martha" is a German opera, and its correct title ought not to have caused bewilderment.

I shall not attempt to reconcile the discrepancies which have found their way into the opera's history, but shall in the following account set down the facts as they seem established in my mind. In 1843 Flotow, the son of a member of the minor nobility of Mecklenburg, was a young composer in Paris, where he had made his serious musical studies under Reicha. He had already set a number of small operas which had been performed in amateur circles, and was looking with longing eyes toward the Opéra-Comique, where his models had won their successes. One day he received a visit from the Marquis de Saint-Georges, first of French librettists after Scribe and collaborator of Donizetti, Adolphe Adam, Auber, Halévy and other famous composers, who asked him if he would undertake to compose the music for one act of a ballet to be produced at the Grand Opéra. Two other composers, Friedrich B. Burgmüller and Edouard Deldevez, had undertaken the other two acts, and the commission was conditioned upon an agreement to finish the work within four weeks. Flotow accepted the task with gladness, the ballet was written, and after its successful production the young musician learned the reason why the work of musical composition had been divided between three men and its hurried completion insisted upon. The director of the Grand Opéra, under his contract with the French Government, was bound to bring forward a new ballet in three acts each year. As the time approached for the 1844 production the director grew anxious to be quit of his obligation, being apprehensive of failure. His principal dancer was pretty, but, as he then thought, not specially talented, and he foresaw financial failure. He called upon the Government Minister and asked for a dispensation exempting him from the obligation to give the new ballet. Information of his purpose reached the ears of the dancer (later a celebrity in her line known as Adèle Dumilâtre). Grievously hurt in her *amour propre*, she, too, went to the Minister, who informed her that the director's conduct was due to his fear that, under the circumstances, an expenditure of 100,000 francs, which the new ballet would cost, would be unjustifiable. The lady departed, but next day a gentleman called at the ministry and offered to pay 100,000 francs to the director provided a ballet was immediately prepared in which Mlle. Dumilâtre should enact the principal part. The agreement was made; Saint-Georges wrote the book, the composers were commissioned, and within the time agreed upon "Lady Harriette, ou la Servante de Greenwich" was on the boards. The plot of the ballet not only pleased the people, but delighted Flotow, and when, in consequence of the success of "Stradella," he received a commission in 1846 to compose an opera for the *Hofoper* at Vienna, he turned to Saint-Georges's ballet, and from it planned the opera "Martha." The libretto was written by a friend named F. W. Riese, who had taken part in the performance of a little opera entitled "Le duc de Guise" which Flotow composed for a charity entertainment given at the palace of the Princess Czartoryska, one of Chopin's *disciples affectionées*. Riese, who wrote over the pen-name of "W. Friedrich," had previously written the book of "Stradella," and secured its representation in his native city of Hamburg, whence it journeyed to Vienna, where its success was so great as to create the wish for an opera specially composed for the Austrian capital.

There is a story current that Saint-Georges borrowed the fundamental idea of his ballet-plot from the personal experience of two of his lady friends who had amused themselves by masquerading as servants at a country fair. The tale is of doubtful authenticity. The genesis of "Lady Harriette, ou la Servante de Greenwich," was like that of many another stage piece. It was modelled after a vaudeville entitled "La Comtesse d'Egmont," which in turn derived its *motif* from the "Ballet des Chambrières à louer," a popular piece in the early part of the seventeenth century. Less than a month after the production of "Martha" in Vienna, W. M. Balfe brought forward an opera based on the same story in London, the book of which had been prepared by Fitzball, whose play on the subject of the Flying Dutchman is supposed to have figured in the genesis of Wagner's opera. According to a statement made by Max Maretzek in his "Sharps and Flats," Balfe told him in 1847 that he had heard "Martha" at Vienna in the preceding summer. He liked the music, but thought the libretto the better part of the work, and so got Fitzball to remodel the story under the title "The Maid of Honour," for which he composed the music, producing the opera in London on December 20th, 1847. He comforted himself with the reflection that if Flotow's opera ever reached London, he, Balfe, would have the advantage of the first impression in his favor. It took "Martha" nearly eleven years to reach London, but it does not appear that "The Maid of Honour" was in any wise responsible for the tardy production. Paris was only four months earlier, and the opera did not make a conclusive hit in the French capital until it was cast in a French version by Saint-Georges and illuminated by Nilsson's genius in 1865. Since "Martha" was not given in Vienna, where it had its first representation, until November 25th, 1847, less than four weeks before the appearance of Balfe's opera in London, it seems certain that unless Maretzek blundered in the telling of the story, Balfe must have heard Flotow's music in private, a circumstance which would throw an unamiable light upon his choice of the subject for himself. Flotow composed the music after he had left Paris (soon after the production of Saint-Georges's ballet in 1844) on his estates in Wutzig and Teutendorf, Pomerania, and in Vienna, putting the finishing touches to it while the rehearsals were in progress in the summer of 1847.

In the original form of the opera and also in the English version the time of the action is supposed to be in the reign of Queen Anne, that is, the early part of the eighteenth century. For an inexplicable reason the period was moved back to the fifteenth century in the Italian version, and forward to the nineteenth in the French. The scene is laid in the old market town of Richmond in Yorkshire and its vicinity. *Lady Harriet* (or *Henrietta*, according to some versions), who is maid of honor to Queen Anne, wearied of the ceaseless round of conventional pleasures at court, conceives and carries out a project which promises to furnish diversion of a novel sort. Disguised as menials, she, her maid and her doting but somewhat aged cousin, *Sir Tristram Mickleford*, are to go to Richmond, whither a band of servants that pass her window are wending their way, and mingle with the crowd at the annual fair. There the frolicsome dames find the servingmaids hiring themselves to the farmers who have come to the fair to engage help. Among the farmers are *Plunkett* and his foster-brother *Lionel*, the latter a waif who had been left as a child at the door of *Plunkett's* father with nothing to identify him except a ring, which in case of need was to be shown to the queen. In furtherance of their prank, *Lady Harriet* (now known as *Martha*) and *Nancy* engage themselves as servants to *Lionel* and *Plunkett*, who are fascinated by their beauty and archness; and carry the joke so far as to accept the legal earnest-money. *Sir Tristram*, who has been pestered by the fair folk, purchases release from their torments with a purse and returns to bid the ladies go back to their homes. They are willing, but *Lionel* and *Plunkett* insist upon their rights under the law, and they are obliged to drive off with the young farmers. Arrived at the farmhouse, an attempt is made to set the young women to work, but in vain, and the men find themselves obliged to instruct them even in the simple art of spinning. *Lionel* loses his heart to *Martha*, who at his solicitation sings "The Last Rose of Summer." The clock rings midnight and the men go to bed, while the women are rescued from their awkward predicament by *Sir Tristram*. In the next scene the foster-brothers discover their quondam servants in the hunting train of Queen Anne. They assert their supposed right, but are repulsed, and when *Lionel* laments the harshness of my lady, who had masqueraded only to make mock of his peace of mind, *Lady Harriet* asks pity for him from the courtiers who come to her aid, on the ground that he is insane. In his despair he sends the ring given to him by his unknown father to the queen, and by its means is identified as the Earl of Derby, son of the old Earl, who had been banished from the kingdom, though guiltless of the offence with which he was charged. Despite her apparent harshness, *Lady Harriet* loves *Lionel*, even before the discovery of his high rank; now she seeks to throw herself into his arms; but he, whose mind has been turned awry by his sufferings, repulses her. In this dilemma a remedy is sought in the device of bringing back to his mind the scene of the first meeting. The fair scene of the first act is reënacted, and amid its merriment reason returns to the lover, and with it happiness. Roguish *Nancy* becomes the prize of *Plunkett*.

"Martha" had its first performance in Vienna on November 25th, 1847. Its growth in popularity was rapid and lasting in Germany, thanks to its gracious and graceful melodiousness; but singularly slow in Italy, France and England, which countries it did not reach until eleven years after its first production. New York listened to its measures in 1852, six years before the privilege of hearing it was vouchsafed to Paris and London. How this came about I have been unable to learn, and the fact itself was unknown to Flotow's biographer. In September, 1852, an English company, under the management of Madame Anna Thillon and Mrs. Maeder, began an engagement at Niblo's Garden, alternating with a French opera company. The new opera was brought forward on November 1st, 1852, under the title "Martha; or, the Richmond Market." Madame Anna Bishop, the wife of Sir Henry Rowley Bishop, who had eloped with Bochsa, the harp virtuoso, in 1839, sang the part of *Lady Harriet*, and Bochsa conducted the performance. The other parts were distributed as follows: *Nancy*, Miss Rosa Jacques; *Lionel*, Signor Guidi; *Plunkett*, Mr. Leach; *Mickleford*, Signor Strini; *the Sheriff*, Mr. Rudolph. The opera was given seven times. In 1855 it was performed in German at Niblo's by the company headed by Fräulein Lehman, and the next year it was heard at the Academy of Music with Madame Lagrange as *Lady Harriet*. This was still two years before the opera reached Paris and London. In the former city it was given in Italian at the Salle Ventadour, on February 11th, 1858, with the parts in the hands of Mesdames Saint-Urbain and Nantier-Didiée (or Alboni) and Messieurs Mario and Graziani. The engagement of Madame Nantier-Didiée and the Signori Mario and Graziani for the season of 1858, at the Royal Opera, at Covent Garden, resulted in the production of the opera in London on July 1st of that year, with Madame Bosio as *Lady Harriet*. On October 11th, 1858, it was given in English at Drury Lane with Miss Louisa Pyne as *Lady Harriet*, Miss Susan Pyne as *Nancy*, and Mr. Harrison as *Lionel*. In 1865 Saint-Georges made a French translation of the libretto for a revival of the opera at the Théâtre Lyrique, where with Madame Nilsson in the titular rôle it had a run of three hundred performances. Madame Adelina Patti, Fanny Natali, Signor Brignoli and Carl Formes (the original *Plunkett*) appeared in the opera when it was given in Philadelphia, on October 10th, 1860, in honor of the then Prince of Wales, now King Edward VII.; and Madame Patti chose it for the performance at the Academy of Music, New York, on November 26th, 1884, with which she celebrated the twenty-fifth anniversary of her entrance on an operatic career.

H. E. KREHBIEL.

NEW YORK, October 2d, 1901.

Index.

Act III.

Act IV.

Appendix

MARTHA

rit.
a tempo
'Cello
Vl.
p
Hn.
Str.
dim.
pp
Bssn.
Allegro vivace.
leggierm.
p
Str.
p
Tutti
Str.
cresc.

p Tutti
Str.
p
Tutti
f Tutti
p Str.
f
ff
Str.
marcato
Tutti
marcato
Str.
Tutti
8
Str.
dol. pp Bssn. & Hns. sustain

meno mosso
Triangle & Side-drum
Hns. & Bssn.
Ob.&Cl.
Tutti
Ob.&Cl.
Hns. & Bssn.
Tutti
f
p
f
p
f
p
f
p
Tempo I.
ff Tutti

8
p
p
Str.
Tromb.
Str.
Tromb.
Str.
Fl.Picc.&Vl.
Tromb.
leggiermente
Str.
Wind sustain
cresc.

Tutti
Cl.
pp
Hns. & Bssn.
Str.
Meno mosso.
f Triangle & Side-dr.
Hns. & Bssn.
p
Fl. & Ob.
Tutti
Fl. & Ob.
Hns. & Bssn.
Tutti
f
p
Vl.
p e sempre dim.
Ob.
Vl.
Ob.
pp
K-dr.
'Cello & Bass

string.
Bssn. & Vla.
p
Ob. Cl. & Vl.
Fl. & Picc.
cresc.
f
Andante.
ff Tutti
rit.
Allegro vivace.
tr

Act I.

Boudoir of Lady Harriet; window in centre and a door at each side. A toilet-table, chairs, &c. Lady Harriet is seated by the table.

Nº 1. Introduction.— „Darf mit nächtig düstren Träumen.“

Flutes, Oboes, Clarinets in C, Bassoons, Horns in G and D, Trumpets in D, Trombones and Ophicleide, Kettledrums in D and G, and Strings.

SOPRANO I.
Sorgfalt beut, Pracht-gestein und sammtne Hül-le, was nur Herz, und Au- - ge freut, ja, was das Au - ge freut.
verted gaze, See the gems that love would proffer, Come, let joy il - lume thy days, let joy il-lume thy days.
SOPRANO II.
Sorgfalt beut, Pracht-gestein und sammtne Hül-le, was nur, nur Herz, was nur Herz und Au-ge freut, ja, was das Au - ge freut.
verted gaze, See the gems that love would proffer, Oh come, oh come, come, let joy il-lume thy days, let joy il-lume thy days.
ALTO.
Sorgfalt beut, Pracht-gestein und sammtne Hül-le, was nur, nur Herz, was nur Herz und Au-ge freut, ja, was das Au-ge freut.
verted gaze, See the gems that love would proffer, Oh come, oh come, come, let joy il-lume thy days, let joy il-lume thy days.
Fl. & Vl.
Nancy.
N.
Sieh' der Ga-ben rei-che Fül-le, was das Au - ge freut, sieh' der Ga-ben rei-che Fül-le, was das Au - ge freut, was das
Now have done with sor-row, come, let joy il-lume thy days, now have done with sor-row, come, let joy il - lume thy days, yes, il-
Sieh' der Ga-ben rei-che Fül-le, was das Au - ge freut, was das
Now have done with sor-row, come, let joy il - lume thy days, yes, il-
Sieh' der Ga-ben rei-che Fül-le, was das Au - ge freut, was das
Now have done with sor-row, come, let joy il - lume thy days, yes, il-

N.
Au - ge freut.
lume thy days.
Au - ge freut.
lume thy days.
Au - ge freut.
lume thy days.
Tutti
ff
Str.
p
N.
H.
Lady Harriet.
Blü-then, die Sir Tri-stan pflückte- Fort da-mit! ihr Duft be-täubt.
Look, Sir Tris-tram sends you flowers- Take them hence, they vex my sight.
Nancy.
Lady H.
Für-stenschmuck, du Hoch-beglückte! Glanz, vor dem mein Aug' sich
See these diamonds! sparkling showers! Ah, to me they are not
Più animato. Nancy. Lady H. Nancy. Lady H.
ad lib.
sträubt! Aber- Lasst mich! Herrin- Ei-let! lasst der Ein-samkeit mich weih'n, meine
bright! Lady- Leave me! Listen- Leave me! My de-sire a-gain I'll own. Ye shall
Aber- Herrin-
Lady- lis-ten-
Aber- Herrin-
Lady- lis-ten-
Più animato.
f

a tempo
H.
Freu-de sei ge-thei-let, mei-nen Schmerz trag' ich al-lein!
share my ev-'ry pleasure, But my grief I'll bear a-lone.
Darf mit näch-tig düstren Träumen
Why must ev-'ry joy be ban-ish'd?
Darf mit näch-tig düstren Träumen
Why must ev-'ry joy be ban-ish'd?
Cl. & Hns.
p colla voce
a tempo
Str.
Schwer-muth dei-ne Stirn um-zieh'n, dei-ne Stir-ne um-zieh'n? Soll aus die-sen
Long e-nough thy heart hath griev'd, long e-nough thou hast griev'd; Pleasure from these
Schwer-muth dei-ne Stirn um-zieh'n, dei-ne Stir-ne um-zieh'n? Soll aus die-sen
Long e-nough thy heart hath griev'd, long e-nough thou hast griev'd; Pleasure from these
Nancy.
N.
O!
See,
hei-t'ren Räumen Lust und Fröhlich-keit ent-flieh'n, soll die Lust uns ent-flieh'n?
halls hath van-ish'd, Since so sore thou wert be-reav'd, thou so sore wert be-reav'd.
hei-t'ren Räumen Lust und Fröhlich-keit ent-flieh'n, soll die Lust uns ent-flieh'n?
halls hath van-ish'd, Since so sore thou wert be-reav'd, thou so sore wert be-reav'd.

N.
sieh' der Ga-ben rei-che Fül-le, die des Freundes Sorgfalt beut, Pracht-ge-stein und
all that art and wealth can of-fer Courts thy sad, a-vert-ed gaze, See the gems that
pp
Sieh' der Ga-ben rei-che Fül-le, die des Freundes Sorgfalt beut, Prachtgestein und
All that art and wealth can of-fer Courts thy sad, a-vert-ed gaze, See the gems that
pp
Sieh' der Ga-ben rei-che Fül-le, die des Freundes Sorgfalt beut, Prachtgestein und
All that art and wealth can of-fer Courts thy sad, a-vert-ed gaze, See the gems that
Str.
Lady H.
H.
Ach, lasst mich al-
Ah, my grief I'll
Nancy.
N.
sammt-ne Hül-le, was nur Herz und Au-ge
love would prof-fer, Come let joy il-lume thy
sammtne Hül-le, was nur, nur Herz, was nur Herz und Au-ge
love would prof-fer, Oh come, oh come, come, let joy il-lume thy
sammtne Hül-le, was nur, nur Herz, was nur Herz und Au-ge
love would prof-fer, Oh come, oh come, come, let joy il-lume thy
Fl. & Ob.
H.
lein, lasst mich al-lein, ach, lasst mich al-
bear, I'll bear a-lone! Ah, I'd be a-
N.
freut, ja, was das Au-ge freut. Ach, lasst sie al-
days, let joy il-lume thy days. Ah, leave her a-
freut, ja, was das Au-ge freut.
days, let joy il-lume thy days.
freut, ja, was das Au-ge freut.
days, let joy il-lume thy days.

H.
cresc.
lein,
lone,
al-
a-
N.
lein,
lone,
al-
a-
Kommt, lasst sie al-
Come, leave her a-
Kommt, lasst sie al-
Come, leave her a-
Tutti cresc.
f
lein, al - lein!
lone, a - lone!
(Exit Chorus.)
ff
p
Str. Wind

Nº 2. Recit. and Duet. — „Von den edlen Kavalieren.“

N.
Ka - va - lie - ren, die den Hof der Kö - nig in und sich sel-ber weidlich zie-ren,
gal - lant no - bles Who the re - gal court a-dorn, Is there one thy spir - it troubles,
p Str.
zog wohl Ei - ner als Ge - winn Eu - er Herz-chen zu sich hin.
One who made thee doff thy scorn? One for whom thou art for-lorn,
Wind
Str.
ad lib.
tr
Lady H.
N. H.
Darf man endlich gratu - li - ren, darf man gratu - li - ren? Eit - ler
Who thy ev'ry joy re-doubles, who thy joy re-dou - bles? Ah, for -
Str.
H.
Wahn! nicht kann mich freu - en sol - che fa - de
bear! no joy or plea - sure Hath my wea - ri -
Fl. Picc. & Ob.
leggiero
Fl. & Ob.
Lie - be - lei, nicht ver - mag mich zu zer - streu - en
ness be - guil'd; Naught on earth that I can trea - sure,
p

rit.
tr
leeres Wort und Schmeichelei.
Joy on me ne'er yet hath smil'd.
Nancy.
Euch umgiebt der Reichthums Fülle,
You are born to pomp and splendor,
rit.
Wind
Und aus Gold und Purpur-hülle gähnt erschöpft die
All that wealth to me can render Is annull'd by
Gnad' und Ehr' wird euch zu Theil.
Ev-'ry joy to you is free.
Str.
Langeweil', ach! ja, die Langeweil'!
grim ennui, alas! by grim ennui!
Poco più animato.
Das ist traurig, ach! und
She must not be left to
Tutti
Str.
Ach, ach, ach, so traurig, ach, ach, ach, so
Ah, what spell of sorrow, ah, what weight of
trübe, solch ein Loos nennt man Gewinn? Wenn ich hier nicht Wunder übe, welkt das zarte Blümlein
languish, Wit shall find a way to aid; If to long a prey to anguish, Soon this tender flow'r will
Bssn. & Hns. sustain

H.
trü-be schleicht im Glanz mein Le-ben hin, was ich
anguish, On my life For- tune hath laid! Am I
N.
hin, das ist traurig,ach,und trü-be,solch ein Loos nennt man Ge-winn? Wenn ich
fade, She must not be left to languish,Wit must find a way to aid, If too
cresc.
thu-e, was ich ü-be,nichts er-freu-et mei-nen Sinn,nichts er-freu-et mei-nen
on-ly born to lan-guish,Ah, is joy for ev-er fled?ah, is joy for ev-er
hier nicht Wunder ü-be,welkt das zar-te Blüm-lein hin,welkt das zar-te Blüm-lein
long a prey to anguish,Soon this tender flow'r will fade, soon this tender flow'r will
Sinn, ach, ach, ach, mei-nen Sinn, was ich thu-e, was ich ü-be,nichts er-
fled, ah, ah, for ev-er fled, am I on-ly born to languish, ah, is
hin, ach, welkt das Blüm-lein hin, wenn ich hier nicht Wunder ü-be,welkt das
fade, ah, soon this flow'r will fade, if too long a prey to anguish,soon this
Ob. & Cl.
Str.
hei-tert mei-nen Sinn,nichts er-hei-tert mei-nen Sinn, ach, nichts er-
joy for ev-er fled, ah, is joy for ev-er fled, ah, is it
zar-te Blümlein hin, wenn ich hier nicht Wun-der ü-be, welkt das
tender flow'r will fade, if too long a prey to an-guish, soon this
Tutti

H.
hei - tert mei - nen Sinn.
then for ev - er fled?
N.
zar - te Blüm-lein hin.
ten - der flow'r will fade.
ff
pp Str.
Nancy.
Fes-te, Bäl-le und Tur-nie-re, wo nur Eu - re Far-be siegt, flat-ternd
Balls and tour-naments in-vite thee, Gallant knights thy col-ors wear, When the
Vl.
hoch von dem Pa-nie - - re, wäh-rend, ach, der Held sich
flash-ing spears af - fright - thee; 'Tis for thee they do and
Ob. & Cl. sustain
schmiegt und dem Dan-kes-blick er-liegt, der ihn traf trotz dem Vi - sie - - re.
dare, Glad thy smil-ing glance to share; Doth such glo-ry not de-light - thee?
Lady H.
Was ich ges - tern heiss er - seh-net, ist's er-
Ev - 'ry-thing my heart could plea-sure, When 'tis
Ob. & Cl.

H.
füllt, so freut's mich kaum, was ich mir als Glück ge-wäh-net, zeigt Ge-
mine, I cast a-way, All that oth-er maid-ens treasure, Meets me
wäh-rung mir als Traum. Der Für-stin Hul-di-
on-ly to be-tray. The pride of wealth and
Nancy.
N.
Fes-te, Bäl-le und Tur-nie-re, wo nur
Balls and tournaments in-vite thee, Gallant
Fl. & Ob.
Vl.
Cl.
Str.
gun-gen, Preis der Mo-de, Ü-ber-fluss,
sta-tion, Leaves me joy-less, lone and sad,
Eu-re Far-be siegt, flat-ternd hoch von dem Pa-nie-re, während
knights thy col-ors wear, When the flashing spears af-fright thee, 'Tis for
trifft mich freud-los, kaum er-run-gen und nichts
Vain are splen-dor, rank, and fa-shion, They ne'er
ach, der Held sich schmiegt und dem Dankes-blick er-liegt, der ihn traf trotz dem Vi-
thee they do and dare, Glad thy smil-ing glance to share; Doth such glo-ry not de-

H.
bleibt als Ü - ber - druss, nichts bleibt als Ü - ber - druss.
made a mourn-er glad, they ne'er made mourn-er glad.
N.
sie-re, dem Vi- sie - re.
light thee, not de - light thee?
cresc.
f Tutti
Nancy.
Ja! dann wär' zu Eu - rem Hei-le nur ein Mit-tel noch ge-blie-ben,
Well, if all re - sourc - es fail us, th'on-ly cure I can dis-cov-er
p Vl. & Cello pizz.
Fl.
Vl. & Vla. arco
Ossia.
ritard.
müsst Ihr sterb-lich Euch ver-lie-
That the pa - tient choose a lov-
ritard.
wie ge - sagt, in höch-ster Ei - le müsst Ihr sterblich Euch ver-lie - ben.
Is, as all wise wo - men tell us, That the pa-tient choose a lov - er.
Vl. & Cello pizz.
Str. arco
ritard.
Lady H.
Ach, ach, ach, so traurig,
Ah, what spell of sorrow,
a tempo
Das ist traurig, ach, und trü-be, solch ein Loos nennt man Gewinn? Wenn ich hier nicht Wunder
She must not be left to languish, Wit shall find a way to aid, If too long a prey to
a tempo
p Str.

H.
ach, ach,_ ach, so trübe schleicht im Glanz mein___ Le-ben
ah, what_weight of anguish On my life For - tune hath
N.
ü-be, welkt das zarte Blümlein hin. Das ist traurig, ach, und trübe, solch ein Loos nennt man Ge-
anguish, Soon this tender flow'r will fade, She must not be left to languish, Wit must find a way to
H.
cresc.
hin, was ich thu-e, was ich ü-be, nichts er-freu-et mei-nen Sinn, nichts er-
laid; Am I on-ly born to languish, Ah, is joy for ev-er fled, ah, is
N.
cresc.
winn? Wenn ich hier nicht Wunder ü-be, welkt das zarte Blüm-lein hin, welkt das
aid, If too long a prey to anguish, Soon this tender flow'r will fade, soon this
cresc.
H.
freu-et mei-nen Sinn, ach, ach,_ ach, mei-nen Sinn, was ich thu-e, was ich
joy for ev-er fled, ah, ah,_ for ev-er fled? Am I_ on-ly born to
N.
zarte Blümlein hin, ach, welkt_ das Blüm-lein hin, wenn ich hier nicht Wun-der
tender flow'r will fade, ah, soon_ this flow'r will fade, If too long a prey to
Ob. & Cl.
f
p Str.
H.
ü-be, nichts er-hei-tert mei-nen Sinn, nichts er-hei-tert mei-nen Sinn, ach,_
languish, Ah, is joy for ev-er fled, ah, is joy for ev-er fled, ah,_
f
N.
f
ü-be, welkt das zar-te Blüm-lein hin, wenn ich hier nicht Wunder ü-be,_
anguish, Soon this tender flow'r will fade, if too long a prey to an-guish,
cresc.
f Tutti

Presto.
H.
nichts er - hei - tert mei - nen Sinn.
is it then for ev - er fled?
N.
welkt das zar - te Blüm - lein hin.
soon this ten - der flow'r will fade.
Presto.
ff Tutti
ad lib.
p a tempo
ach!
Ah!
p
a tempo
pp str. legato
f Tutti
Str.
pp

H.
ach, nein, nichts er-
ah, for ev-er
N.
ach, ja, solch ein
ah, this flow'r will
freut, ach, mei-nen Sinn, ach, mei-nen Sinn,
fled, ah, ah, is joy for ev-er fled?
Loos, ach, nennt man Ge-winn, nennt man Ge-winn,
fade, ah, too soon this ten-der flow'r will fade,
f Tutti
ach, ach, den
ah, ah, 'tis
ach, ach, ach, Ge-
ah, ah, soon will
Sinn!
fled!
winn!
fade!
ff

No. 3. Terzet.— „Schöne Lady und Cousine."

(Same Score.)

Nancy. Tristram. Lady H. Tristram.
N. T. H.
Wei-ter, My-lord, es wird spät. Wollte fra-gen Nun, so fra-get Ob Sie
Welcome is your court-ly mien. I would ask ye Say your plea-sure. Had your
f Tutti p Cl. & Bssn. Str. pizz. Hns.
Lady H.
T. H.
sanft zu ruh'n ge-ruht? ob der Tag zur Freude ta-get? Gieb ihm
la-dy-ship good rest? To es-court ye I'm at lei-sure. Pray dis-
8
f Vl. Fl. & Picc. Bssn. p Cl. & Bssn. Str. pizz. mf Wind
Nancy. Tristram.
H. N. T.
Ant-wort. Leid-lich gut. Nach Be-lie-ben, Lust-barkei-ten
patch him. Vain your quest. Great at-tractions claim at-ten-tion,
p Str. arco Hns. Vl. p dolce Str.
T.
vor-zuschlagen, bin so frei: Hah-nen-kampf und E-sel-
There's a cock-fight just be-low; And the don-key-fair I'd
Nancy. Tristram (tenderly).
T. N.
rei-ten My-lord, sind doch auch da-bei? Ein Spa-zier-gang
men-tion. Surely you in-tend to go? Come a-walk-ing

Lady H.
Tristram.
Lady H.
H.
T.
Ich verzichte! Pfer - de-ren-nen — Oh! ich weiss,
Pray excuse me. Or the rac-es — I de-cline,
wie ge-ring Sie von Ge-wichte — und wie sicher — d'rum der
Fights and rac - es don't a-muse me, Their at-tractions I — re-
rit.
a tempo
Preis! Ha! — der Narrheit oh - ne — Gleichen, oh - ne
sign. Ah, — what — fol-ly, what de - lu-sion, what de -
Nancy.
N.
Ha! der Narr-heit oh - ne Gleichen! sol-che Ein-falt sah man —
Ah, what fol-ly, what de - lu-sion, Would the an-cient fop were —
Tristram.
Ha! sie lä-chelt, gu-tes Zei-chen, mei-ne Lie-be rüh-ret,
Ah, she blush-es sweet con - fu-sion, Now my hopes, my hopes be -
Str. Hns. & Bssn.
Glei - chen! ha, — sol-che Ein-falt —
lu-sion! Ah, — bid the an-cient —
nie; Lie-be will der Thor er-rei-chen, träumt von See-len -
gone, To be rid of this in-tru-sion, Shy-ness I — must —
rüh-ret sie. Sprödes Herz, dich zu er-wei-chen, for-dert Klug-heit
gin — to — dawn; 'tis no glamour, no il - lu-sion, I this tim-id
f
p
Tutti

H.
sah man nie, ha, Lie - be
fop be - gone. Ah, I'd be
N.
har-mo - nie, Narr-heit oh - ne Glei-chen, sol - che
quite dis - own. Ah, what fol - ly, what de - lu - sion,
T.
und Ge - nie, gu - tes, gu - tes Zei-chen, mei - ne
heart have won, 'Tis no gla - mour, no il - lu - sion,
p Str.
f Tutti
p Str.
Wind
H.
will der Thor - er - rei - chen, ha,
rid of this in - tru - sion, Ah,
N.
Ein - falt sah man nie, Narr-heit oh - ne Glei-chen,
would the fop were gone, ah what fol - ly, what de -
T.
Lie - be rüh - ret sie, gu - tes, gu - tes Zei-chen,
sure her heart is won, 'tis no gla - mour, no il -
f Tutti
p Str.
Wind
H.
traümt von See-len - har - mo - nie!
leave me, pray, a - while a - lone!
N.
sol - che Ein-falt sah man nie!
lu - sion, would the fop were gone!
T.
mei - ne Lie - be rüh - ret sie, ha! sie lä-chelt, gu-tes Zeichen,
lu - sion, sure her heart is won. Ha, she blushes sweet con-fu-sion,
Picc. & Ob.
8

sah— man
were— he
Nancy. calando
solche Einfalt, sol-che Ein-falt sah-man—
Ah what fol-ly, what de-lu-sion, were he—
Tristram.
meine Lie-be rühret sie, mei - ne Lie-be rüh-ret
I am cer-tain she is won, I am cer-tain she is
Str. calando
a tempo
Lady H.
Ja,— der— Narrheit oh - ne— Gleichen, oh - ne
Ah— what fol - ly, what— de - lu-sion, what de -
nie, der Narrheit oh - ne Gleichen, sol - che Einfalt sah— man—
gone, what fol - ly, what de - lu - sion, would the an-cient fop— were—
sie, ha, sie lächelt, gu - tes Zei-chen, mei - ne Lie-be rüh-ret,
won, ha, she blushes sweet con - fu-sion, now my hopes, my hopes be -
a tempo
p Str. Hns. & Bssn.
Glei - chen, ha,— träumt von See-len -
lu - sion, ah,— bid the an - cient—
nie, Lie-be will der Thor er - rei-chen, träumt von See-len -
gone, to be rid of this in - tru-sion, ev - 'ry shy-ness—
rüh - ret— sie, sprödes Herz, dich zu er - wei-chen, for - dert Klug-heit
gin— to— dawn, 'tis no glamour, no il - lu-sion, I this tim-id
f
p
f Tutti

ad lib.
cresc.
H.
harmonie, träumt von Seelenharmonie, ach!
fop begone, bid the ancient fop begone, ah!
N.
harmonie, träumt von Seelenharmonie, ach!
I'll disown, ev'ry shyness I'll disown, ah!
T.
und Genie, fordert Klugheit und Genie, ach!
heart have won, I this timid heart have won, ah!
p Str.
Wind
Str. cresc.
f Tutti
a tempo
von Harmonie.
bid him begone.
Harmonie.
were he gone.
und Genie.
Yes, I've won.
Più allegro.
Sir!
Thanks,
Carousel!
Would you drive?
Più allegro.
Vl.
pp stacc.
Lady H.
meinen Fächer!
I've the vapors.
Str.
Tristram.
Lady H.
(Tristram fetches it; exhausted)
T.
H.
Wasserfahrt!
Or a row?
Sir! mein Flacon!
Give me my fan.
Vl.
stacc.
Str.

Nancy (aside).
N.
Die Lie - be, die Liebe wird schon schwä -
Al - read - y his ardent love is wan-
Lady H.
H.
cher! S'ist kalt im Pa-vil - lon! schliessen Sie das Fen-ster ei-lig.
ing. I'm cold, there is a draught! Pray, Sir Tristram, shut the window.
f
Vl.
p stacc.
Tristram (shuts it).
T.
Hetzjagd!
Slav'ry!
Str.
Lady H.
H.
T.
Oh! Wie wird es heiss! Luft! das Fen-ster
Oh! now it's too hot! Air! the win-dow
Tristram.
Öff-nen?
Shall I?
f
Lady H. Nancy.
(Sir Tristram sinks into a seat)
H.
N.
Frei-lich! My-lord läuft um den Preis!
O - pen. You've the fond lover's lot.
ff Tutti

H.
Ha, der Narrheit oh - ne Glei-chen, oh - ne
Ah, what fol - ly, what de - lu - sion, what de -
Nancy.
N.
Ha, der Narr-heit oh - ne Gleichen, sol - che Ein-falt sah man
Ah, what fol - ly, what de - lu - sion, Would the an - cient fop were
Tristram.
T.
Gu - tes Zei - chen, gu - tes Zei - chen, mei - ne Lie - be rüh - ret,
Ha, she blushes sweet con - fu - sion, Now my hopes, my hopes be -
p Str. Bssn. & Hns.
Glei - chen, ha, träumt von See - len -
lu - sion, Ah, bid the an - cient
nie, Lie - be will der Thor er - rei - chen, träumt von See - len -
gone, To be rid of this in - tru - sion, Shy - ness I must
rüh - ret sie, sprödes Herz, dich zu er - wei - chen, for - dert Klug - heit
gin to dawn, 'Tis no glamour, no il - lu - sion, I this tim - id
f
p
f Tutti
ad lib.
cresc.
har - mo - nie, träumt von See - len - har - mo - nie, ach!
fop be - gone, bid the an - cient fop be - gone, Ah!
har - mo - nie, träumt von See - len - har - mo - nie, ach!
quite dis - own, shy - ness I must quite dis - own, ah!
und Ge - nie, for - dert Klug - heit und Ge - nie, ja!
heart have won, I this tim - id heart have won, yea!
p Str.
Wind
Str. cresc.
f Tutti

a tempo
H.
N.
T.
_von Har - mo - nie, ja!_von See - len - har - mo - nie, ja!_von See - len-
bid him be - gone, ah,_I'd be a - while a - lone, ah,_I'd be a -
Har - mo - nie, ja!_von See - len - har - mo - nie, ja!_von See - len-
were_ he gone! would the an - cient fop were gone, would the an - cient
und_ Ge - nie, for - dert Klug - heit und Ge - nie, for - dert Klug - heit
Yea,_ I've won, I this tim - id heart have won, I her gen - tle
f
p Str.
har - mo - nie, ja!_von See - len - har - mo - nie!
while a - lone, ah,_I'd be a - while_ a - lone!
har - mo - nie, ja!_von See - len - har - mo - nie!
fop were gone, would the an - cient fop_ were gone!
und Ge - nie, for - dert Klug - heit und_ Ge - nie!
heart have won, I this tim - id heart_ have won!
f Tutti

Chorus of Maid-servants.—„Wohlgemuth, junges Blut."

Tristram.
Nancy.
T.
N.
Froh? Bah! un - gemein gemein! Wie
That? Bah! Ser-vant girls, how low! How
p
f
reg', nimmer träg', wandern wir mit lust'gem Sang, gu-ter Ding', froh er - kling' un-ser
home we have come, Blithe-ly sing-ing on our way, Mas-ter kind we would find, We have
Tristram.
N.
T.
froh das klinget! Kann solch' Volk so glücklich sein?
gay their singing! Who'd a thought on them bestow?
Chor den Pfad ent - lang; immer reg', nimmer träg', wandern wir mit lust'gem Sang, gu-ter
donn'd our best ar - ray; Far from home we have come, Blithely sing - ing on our way, Master
Lady H.
più animato
Nancy. Recit.
H.
N.
Glück - lich, wer so harm - los singet! Oh! nun
Joy is in their care - less singing! I re -
Ding', froh er - kling' un-ser Chor den Pfad ent-lang.
kind we would find, We have donn'd our best ar-ray.
Recit.
ff Tutti
p Str.
più animato

a tempo
N.
weiss ich! Markt ist heute, wo die Mäg-de sich ver-mie-then,
member why they're singing — Richmond Fair to-day's be-ginning,
hin nach Richmond zieh'n die Leu-te, sich den Pächtern
All the lass-es of the country go a-broad to
Tempo I.
an-zu-bie-ten. Mit dem Än-zel un-term Arm
seek for places. Gay their hats with summer flow'rs,
Wohl-ge-muth, jun-ges Blut, ü-ber Weg, ü-ber Steg, mun-ter
Come a-way, Maid-ens gay, To the fair All re-pair, Let us
Wohl-ge-muth, jun-ges Blut, ü-ber Weg, ü-ber Steg, mun-ter
Come a-way, Maid-ens gay, To the fair All re-pair, Let us
Tempo I.
Wind
und dem Strausse auf dem Hut, erst zum
Each a satchel in her hand, Dancing
fort, hin zum Ort, wo uns Ruh' win-ket zu! Wohl-ge-muth, jun-ges Blut, ü-ber
go, Let us show Will-ing hearts, Fair de-serts! Come a-way, Maid-ens gay, To the
fort, hin zum Ort, wo uns Ruh' win-ket zu! Wohl-ge-muth, jun-ges Blut, ü-ber
go, Let us show Will-ing hearts, Fair de-serts! Come a-way, Maid-ens gay, To the

N.
Tanze zieht der Schwarm, dann zum Werk, mit frohem Muth.
thro' the mer-ry hours, Till they plight the servile bond.
Weg, ü-ber Steg, munter fort, hin zum Ort, wo uns Ruh' win-ket zu!
fair All re-pair, Let us go, Let us show Will-ing hearts, Fair de-serts!
Weg, ü-ber Steg, munter fort, hin zum Ort, wo uns Ruh' win-ket zu!
fair All re-pair, Let us go, Let us show Will-ing hearts, Fair de-serts!
ff Tutti
Tristram.
Nancy.
Lady H.
T.
N.
H.
Dummer Brauch! Gar al-te Sitte! Ach wie hübsch! das möcht' ich
Sil-ly ways! 'Tis ancient custom! I should like to go, I
Vl.
p Str.
H.
seh'n, un-er-kannt dort in der Mit-te der vergnüg-ten Menschen steh'n.
own, And a-mong the joyous people I would roam a while un-known.
Fl. & Vl.
Tristram.
Lady H.
T.
H.
Albern-hei-ten! Sehr ver-bunden! Nun ge-ra-de will ich's thun, weil Sie
Foolish fancies! What po-liteness! Now I am re-solv'd to go, Since Sir

Tristram.
Più animato.
H.
T.
albern es ge-fun - den—
Tristram thinks it fol - ly—
Eu - er Gna-den will ge - ruhn?
Nay, fair la - dy, say not so.
f Tutti
Str.
Wind
Lady H.
Nancy, her die Bauern - mieder von der letz - ten Mas - ke-
Nancy, fetch my rustic bodice, At the fan - cy ball I
Tristram.
Lady H.
ra - de! Wie? Sie las-sen Sich her - nie - der? Das, My - lord, er-
wore it. What?'twould be most un - be - com - ing. Sir, your words of
höht ge - ra - de! Hin zum lus - ti - gen Ga - lopp, hin zum
gal - lant court'sy Quite in - spire me to pro - ceed, quite in -
f Tutti
ad lib.
(laughing)
Allegro.
lus - ti - gen Ga - lopp, Martha, Nan - cy und Sir Bob!
spire me to pro - ceed, Martha, Nan - cy and Old Rob!
f Tutti

Lady H.
Ei! das sind Sie, ei! das sind
Who? why, your-self! who? why, your-
Tristram.
Nancy.
Wer ist Bob? wer ist Bob? Ei! das sind Sie, ei! das sind
Who is Rob? who is Rob? Who? why, your-self! who? why, your-
Ob.
Fl.
p Vl.
'Cello
lento
Sie! Wie? Tristan, ist das Ih-re
self! Tristram. What, Tristram, is that how you
Sie! Nim-mermehr! ich thu's nicht!
self! No, not I, that's too much!
Ob.
f Tutti
colla voce
lento
p Hns. & Bssn.
Lie-be? ist das Ih-re Lie-be? Sie bit-ten? Ich ver-zei-he!
love me? is that how you love me? What sigh-ing? Here's your par-don!
Ach!
Ah!
Cl.
(coquettishly giving him a nosegay)
Andante.
Sieh, Freund Bob, was ich Dir wei-he, ja, Dir weihe!
This, good Rob, shall be your guerdon, ay, your guerdon.
f Str. pizz.

H.
Und jetzt, mun - tre Nan - cy, ü - be ihn zum plum-pen Bau-ern - tanz.
Nan-cy, now be quick and show him How the coun-try peo-ple dance.
T.
Tristram.
Nimmer werd' ich mich ver - ste-hen.
I will not be thus de - graded.
Fl. Picc. & Oboe
Triangle
H.
Bob, hübsch plump! Es wird schon ge-hen. Was man sein will, sei man ganz.
Rob, must you be still up - braided? For your suit here is a chance.
Nancy (showing him the steps).
N.
So recht kräf-tig, derb und hef-tig, lin-kisch, einwärts, auf und ab. - Hut im Nacken, mit den Hacken stampfend, wie im kur-zen Trab.
Upward jumping, downward thumping, Mind you inwards point your toes; Rak-ish feather, Sprig of heather, Youth and fas-ci - na-tion shows.
più animato
p Str. arco
Wind
f
N.
H.
Lady H. (sternly).
Wie ich's woll-te!
Dance, or leave me!
Tristram (tries to dance).
Was? Ich soll-te - Nimmer -
What - you'd have me - No, I
p Str.
f Wind

H.
N.
T.
Nun hin und her!
Do what I want!
Nancy.
Nur hübsch so fort. Denn Übung
Come, there's a dear. I'll show you
mehr! Ich, ein Lord! Ich, ein Lord!
can't! I, a peer! I, a peer!
p Str.
f Wind
p Str.
f Wind
Str.
Andante.
La la la la la la la la la la la
ist die bes-te Lehr'! Tra la la, tra la la
how they dance it here. Tra la la, tra la la
Tristram (dancing).
Andante.
f Tutti
p Str. pizz. & Trgle.
la la la la la la la la la la la la la la la la la la la la la la
la la la la la la la la la la la la
(aside)
Ich, ein Lord!
I, a peer!

Animato.
H.
la la la la la la la la la la la.
la la la la la la la la la la la.
So wird's ge-hen.
Now you've hit it,
ach!
ah!
N.
la la la la la la.
la la la la la la.
Brav sich drehen.
Don't forget it.
T.
Animato.
mf Tutti
p Str.
Nicht so zier-lich, ach,
You're too graceful, ah,
Mehr natürlich, mehr natürlich!
That was almost true to Nature!
Ach! auf Ehr'! ich kann nicht mehr!
'Pon my word, 'tis too ab-surd!
Ach! wie ist Na-
Nature does not
mf
p
ach,
ah,
Mehr na - türlich, mehr na - türlich!
That was almost true to nature.
(falls exhausted into a seat)
tur so schwer!
favor me!
Nein, auf Ehr'! ich kann nicht mehr!
Oh, I'm dead, oh let me be!

Molto animato.
H.
cresc.
ach, ach! Bob, hübsch plump, es wird schon
ah, ah! Bra - vo, Rob, you are im -
N.
cresc.
Ach, ach! Bob, hübsch plump, es wird schon
Ah, ah! Bra - vo, Rob, you are im -
T.
Ach, auf Ehr', ich kann nicht
I'm ex - haust - ed, by the
Molto animato.
p Str. cresc.
f Tutti
ge - hen, Bob, hübsch plump, es wird schon ge - hen, ach,
prov - ing, bra - vo, Rob, you are im - prov - ing, ah,
ge - hen, Bob, hübsch plump, es wird schon geh'n, ach, ach,
prov - ing, All the grac - es fa - vor thee, ah, ah,
mehr, auf Ehr', auf Ehr', ich kann nicht mehr!
Saints, I am ex - haust - ed, let me be!
p Str.
cresc.
Presto.
Bob, hübsch plump, es wird schon ge - hen, Bob, hübsch plump, es wird schon geh'n, ja, gewiss, ja, ge -
Bra - vo, Rob, you are im - prov - ing, Bra - vo, Rob, my partner be, Bravo, Rob, bravo,
Bob, hübsch plump, es wird schon ge - hen Bob, hübsch plump, es wird schon geh'n, ja, gewiss, ja, ge -
Bra - vo, Rob, you are im - prov - ing, All the grac - es fa - vor thee, Bravo, Rob, bravo,
Ach, auf Ehr', ich kann nicht mehr, auf Ehr', auf Ehr', ich kann nicht mehr, ja, gewiss, ja, ge -
I'm ex - hausted, by the Saints, I am ex - haust - ed, let me be, What the fun of this
Presto.
f Tutti

H.
N.
T.
wiss, es wird schon geh'n, ja, ge-wiss, ja, ge-wiss, es wird schon geh'n, nur Muth, nur
Rob, my partner be, bra-vo, Rob, bravo, Rob, my partner be, oh bra-vo,
wiss, es wird schon geh'n, ja, ge-wiss, ja, ge-wiss, es wird schon geh'n, nur Muth, nur
Rob, my partner be, bra-vo, Rob, bravo, Rob, my partner be, oh bra-vo,
wiss, ich kann nicht mehr, ja, ge-wiss, ja, ge-wiss, ich kann nicht mehr, nein,
is, I cannot see, what the fun of this is, I can-not see, no,
(Exit Lady H. and Nancy laughing, with Sir Tristram.)
Muth, es wird schon geh'n, nur Muth, nur Muth, ah, fort!
bra-vo, bra-vo, Rob, my partner be, bra-vo!
Muth, es wird schon geh'n, nur Muth, nur Muth, ah, fort!
bra-vo, bra-vo, Rob, my partner be, bra-vo!
ich kann nicht mehr, nein, nein, nein!
I can-not see, no, no, no!
ff Tutti

Nº 4. Chorus of Farmers.— „Mädchen, brav und treu."

The Market-place at Richmond. Booths. In front of the stage are tables and benches. Tents at the sides.

Flute, Piccolo, Oboes, Clarinets in C, Bassoons, Horns in G & D, Trumpets in C, Trombones, Ophicleide, Kettledrums in G & D, Triangle, Side-drum, Big Drum & Strings (Side-drum on the stage).

Markt ist frei; macht euch fröh-lich auf, im raschen Lauf, wir war-ten drauf! Flink, ihr schmucken
now be-gin, Show your ro - sy fac - es, And our hearts ye soon shall win. Fleet of foot, and
p
marcato
p Str.
Die-ne-rinnen, nur nicht träg' und säumig heut, bald soll hier der Markt begin-nen, wie es al-ter
clad with neatness, Come and let the master choose, Sweet of temper, all discreetness, Who a prize like
Brauch ge-beut; flink, ihr schmucken Die-ne-rin-nen, nur nicht träg' und säumig heut, bald soll hier der
this would lose? Fleet of foot, and clad with neatness, Come and let the master choose, Sweet of temper,

ff p
Markt be-gin-nen, wie es al-ter Brauch ge-beut. Topp, gilt der Han-del, war der
all dis-creet-ness, Who a prize like this would lose? Done is the bar-gain, if the
Tutti Str.
f p
Wan-del rein und un-be-scholten; Topp! sagt der Mie-ther als Ge-bie-ter, stets wird
maid is trust-y, blithe and will-ing; Done, if the hand-sel she ac-cepts, the mas-ter's
Fleiss ver-gol-ten; Topp, gilt der Han-del, war der Wan-del rein und un-be-schol-ten,
prof-fer'd shil-ling; Done is the bar-gain, if the maid is trust-y, blithe and will-ing,

f
ff Tutti
stets wird Fleiss ver-gol-ten. Ihr Mädchen, her-bei!
and she takes the shil-ling; ye lass-es, come on.
stets wird Fleiss ver-gol-ten. Ihr Mädchen, her-bei! Her-bei ihr Mädchen, brav und treu, her-
and she takes the shil-ling; ye lass-es, come on, Come on, ye bright and bux-om lass-es,
bei, herbei, der Markt ist frei; macht Euch fröh-lich auf, im raschen Lauf, wir war-ten drauf!
Come, the fair shall now be-gin, Show your ro-sy fac-es, And our hearts ye soon shall win!
Mäd-chen, brav und treu, her-bei, her-bei, der Markt ist frei; macht Euch fröh-lich auf, im
Bright and bux-om lass-es, Come, the fair shall now be-gin, Show your ro-sy fac-es,

f
ra-schen Lauf, wir war-ten drauf! Her-bei!
And our hearts ye soon shall win. Come on!
ff
ra-schen Lauf, wir war-ten drauf! Flink, ihr schmucken Die-ne-rin-nen, nur nicht träg' und
And our hearts ye soon shall win. Fleet of foot, and clad with neatness, Come and let the
ff
ra-schen Lauf, wir war-ten drauf! Flink, ihr schmucken Die-ne-rin-nen, nur nicht träg' und
And our hearts ye soon shall win. Fleet of foot, and clad with neatness, Come and let the
ff Str. Cl. & Bssn.
Her-bei! Her-bei! Her-bei!
come on! come on! come on!
säumig heut, bald soll hier der Markt be-gin-nen, wie es al-ter Brauch ge-beut!
mas-ter choose, Sweet of tem-per, all discreet-ness, Who a prize like this would lose?
säumig heut, bald soll hier der Markt be-gin-nen, wie es al-ter Brauch ge-beut!
mas-ter choose, Sweet of tem-per, all discreet-ness, Who a prize like this would lose?
Mäd-chen, brav und treu, her-bei, der Markt, der Markt ist frei, Mäd-chen, brav und
Come, ye lass-es all, come on, the fair shall now be-gin, Come, ye lass-es
Mäd-chen, brav und treu, her-bei, der Markt, der Markt ist frei, Mäd-chen, brav und
Come, ye lass-es all, come on, the fair shall now be-gin, Come, ye lass-es
Mäd-chen, brav und treu, her-bei, der Markt, der Markt ist frei, Mäd-chen, brav und
Come, ye lass-es all, come on, the fair shall now be-gin, Come, ye lass-es
f Tutti
p
f

treu, her-bei, der Markt ist frei, her-bei, her-bei, her-bei, her-
all, come on, the fair be-gins, come on, come on, come on, come
treu, her-bei, der Markt ist frei, her-bei, her-bei, her-bei, her-bei, her-
all, come on, the fair be-gins, come on, come on, come on, come on, come
treu, her-bei, der Markt ist frei, her-bei, her-bei, her-bei, her-bei, her-
all, come on, the fair be-gins, come on, come on, come on, come on, come
bei, her-bei, her-bei! Seid will-kommen, seid will-
on, come on, come on! Wel-come all, come forth to
bei, her-bei, her-bei! Seht, sie kommen, seht, sie kommen! Seid will-kommen, seid will-
on, come on, come on! See, they come, now let us greet them, Wel-come all, come forth to
bei, her-bei, her-bei! Seht, sie kommen, seht, sie kommen! Seid will-kommen, seid will-
on, come on, come on! See, they come, now let us greet them, Wel-come all, come forth to
cresc.
kom-men!
meet them!
kom-men!
meet them!
kom-men!
meet them!
ff
Side-dr. & Triangle

Allegretto.
SOPR. I. II.
Chorus of Servantmaids.
ALTO I. II.
Wohl-ge - muth, jun-ges Blut, ü-ber Weg, ü-ber
Come a - way, Maid-ens gay, To the fair All re -
Allegretto.
Ob. & Cl.
p Wind
Steg, munter fort, ging's zum Ort, wo uns Ruh' win-ket zu. Wohl-ge - muth, jun-ges
pair, Let us go, Let us show Willing hearts, Fair de - serts, Come a - way, Maid-ens
Blut, ü-ber Weg, ü-ber Steg, munter fort, hin zum Ort, wo uns Ruh' win-ket
gay, To the fair All re - pair, Let us go, Let us show Will-ing hearts, Fair de -
f
zu. Im-mer reg', nimmer träg', auf dem Weg mit lust'gem Sang', froh er - scholl, hoff-nungs-
serts. Far from home we have come, Blithely sing-ing on our way, Masters kind we would
f Tutti
p

voll, unser Chor den Pfad entlang. Wem nur Lust in der Brust für die Arbeit froh sich
find, We have donn'd our best array. Heart of joy kills annoy, Makes the hand for labor
Chorus of Farmers.
regt, die voll Muth Hab' und Gut, Sack und Pack weiter trägt. Mädchen, brav, brav und
strong; Masters, ask any task, Nor the hiring prolong. Now come on, lasses
Tutti
Chorus of Servantmaids.
treu, nur herbei, der Markt ist frei. Ist's nicht hier, ist es dorten, dass uns winkt Ruh' und
all, for the fair shall soon begin. Far from home have we come, And masters kind we would
Str.

p
Rast. Ist's nicht hier, ist es
find. Far from home have we
Rast. Ist's nicht hier, ist es
find. Far from home have we
Chorus of Farmers.
f
Mädchen, brav, brav und treu, nur her-bei, der Markt ist frei.
Yes, come on, lass-es all, for the fair shall now be-gin.
ff Tutti
p Str.
dor-ten, dass uns winkt Ruh' und Rast. Wohl-ge-muth, jun-ges Blut, ü-ber
come, and masters kind we would find. Come a-way, Maidens gay, To the
Nur her-bei,
Lass-es, come,
Wind

Weg, ü-ber Steg, mun-ter fort ging's zum Ort, wo uns Ruh' win-ket zu; wohl-ge-
fair All re-pair, Let us go, Let us show Will-ing hearts, Fair de-serts, Come a-
Weg, ü-ber Steg, mun-ter fort ging's zum Ort, wo uns Ruh' win-ket zu; wohl-ge-
fair All re-pair, Let us go, Let us show Will-ing hearts, Fair de-serts, Come a-
her-bei, her-bei,
come, lass-es all,
her-bei, her-bei,
come, lass-es all,
her-bei, her-bei,
come, lass-es all,
muth, jun-ges Blut, ü-ber Weg, ü-ber Steg, mun-ter fort ging's zum Ort, wo uns
way, Maidens gay, To the fair All re-pair, Let us go, Let us show Will-ing
muth, jun-ges Blut, ü-ber Weg, ü-ber Steg, mun-ter fort ging's zum Ort, wo uns
way, Maidens gay, To the fair All re-pair, Let us go, Let us show Will-ing
der Markt
the fair
der Markt
the fair
der Markt
the fair

Più animato.
Ruh' winket zu, her-bei, her-bei, her-bei, her-bei, her-bei, her-bei, der Markt ist frei, der Markt ist frei!
hearts, Fair de-serts, we come, we come, we come, we come, we come, we come, the fair be-gins, we come, we come!
ist frei, her-bei, her-bei, her-bei, her-bei, her-bei, her-bei, der Markt ist frei, der Markt ist frei!
be - gins, come, lass-es all, come, lasses all, we come, we come, the fair be-gins, we come, we come!
ist frei, her-bei, her-bei, her-bei, her-bei, her-bei, her-bei, der Markt ist frei, der Markt ist frei!
be - gins, come, lasses all, come, lasses all, come, lass-es all, the fair be-gins, come, lass-es all!
Vl.
f Più animato.

Allegro.
Schnell, wer brav und treu, her-bei, her-bei, der Markt ist frei; doch erst Ruh' und Rast, nach
We are bux-om lass-es, waiting till the fair begins, Ev-'ry ro-sy face to-
Schnell, wer brav und treu, her-bei, her-bei, der Markt ist frei; doch erst Ruh' und Rast, nach
We are bux-om lass-es, waiting till the fair begins, Ev-'ry ro-sy face to-
Schnell, wer brav und treu, her-bei, her-bei, der Markt ist frei; doch erst Ruh' und Rast, nach
Bright and bux-om lass-es, come, the fair shall now be-gin, Show your ro-sy fac-es,
Schnell, wer brav und treu, her-bei, her-bei, der Markt ist frei; doch erst Ruh' und Rast, nach
Bright and bux-om lass-es, come, the fair shall now be-gin, Show your ro-sy fac-es,
Schnell, wer brav und treu, her-bei, her-bei, der Markt ist frei; doch erst Ruh' und Rast, nach
Bright and bux-om lass-es, come, the fair shall now be-gin, Show your ro-sy fac-es,
Allegro.
ff Tutti
Lauf und Hast mit schwerer Last. Mäd-chen, brav und treu, her-bei, herbei, der Markt ist frei,
day a pleasant master wins. We are bux-om lass-es, wait-ing till the fair begins,
Lauf und Hast mit schwerer Last. Mäd-chen, brav und treu, her-bei, herbei, der Markt ist frei,
day a pleasant master wins. We are bux-om lass-es, wait-ing till the fair begins,
Lauf und Hast mit schwerer Last. Mäd-chen, brav und treu, her-bei, herbei, der Markt ist frei,
and our hearts ye soon shall win. Bright and bux-om lass-es, come, the fair shall now begin,
Lauf und Hast mit schwerer Last. Mäd-chen, brav und treu, her-bei, herbei, der Markt ist frei,
and our hearts ye soon shall win. Bright and bux-om lass-es, come, the fair shall now begin,
Lauf und Hast mit schwerer Last. Mäd-chen, brav und treu, her-bei, herbei, der Markt ist frei,
and our hearts ye soon shall win. Bright and bux-om lass-es, come, the fair shall now begin,

doch erst Ruh' und Rast, nach Lauf und Hast mit schwerer Last; her - bei, her - bei, der
ev - 'ry ro - sy face to - day a plea - sant mas - ter wins, we come, we come, the
doch erst Ruh' und Rast, nach Lauf und Hast mit schwerer Last; her - bei, her - bei, der
ev - 'ry ro - sy face to - day a plea - sant mas - ter wins, we come, we come, the
doch erst Ruh' und Rast, nach Lauf und Hast mit schwerer Last; her - bei, her - bei, der
show your ro - sy fac - es, and our hearts ye soon shall win, come on, come on, the
doch erst Ruh' und Rast, nach Lauf und Hast mit schwerer Last; her - bei, her - bei, der
show your ro - sy fac - es, and our hearts ye soon shall win, come on, come on, the
doch erst Ruh' und Rast, nach Lauf und Hast mit schwerer Last; her - bei, her - bei, der
show your ro - sy fac - es, and our hearts ye soon shall win, come on, come on, the
Markt ist frei, her - bei, ja, der Markt ist frei, ja, her - bei, her-
fair be - gins, we come, yea, the fair be - gins, yea, the fair be-
Markt ist frei, her - bei, ja, der Markt ist frei, ja, her - bei, her-
fair be - gins, we come, yea, the fair be - gins, yea, the fair be-
Markt ist frei, her - bei, ja, der Markt ist frei, ja, her - bei, her-
fair be - gins, come on, yea, the fair be - gins, yea, the fair be-
Markt ist frei, her - bei, ja, der Markt ist frei, ja, her - bei, her-
fair be - gins, come on, yea, the fair be - gins, yea, the fair be-
Markt ist frei, her - bei, ja, der Markt ist frei, ja, her - bei, her-
fair be - gins, come on, yea, the fair be - gins, yea, the fair be-

bei, ja, der Markt ist frei, der Markt ist frei, der Markt ist
gins, yea, the fair be-gins, the fair be-gins, the fair be-
frei!
gins!
(They disperse.)

Nº 5. — „Wie das schnattert!"

Same Score (Triangle, Side-drum, and Big Drum excepted).

Allegretto.
Plunkett.
P.
Wie dasschnattert,wie das plappert,
What a chat-ter,what a clat-ter,
Cl.
f Tutti p Str.
p Wind
wie dasdurch-ein-an-der spricht! Gelt! Wenn's bei den Mä-del's
All areshout-ing to be heard. It be-comes a serious
Fl.
p Wind.
happert, ist's für-wahr das Mundwerk nicht. Nun, HerrBruder! Willdoch
matter, How to choose, up-on my word. Well,good brother! Looking
Vl.
Str.
Lionel.
Plunkett.
P.
L.
hof-fen, hastschon ei-neWahl ge-trof-fen? Ach, wo-zu? Wo-zu? Zum
round yet? Is the thingyou look for found yet? Why this haste? This haste? I'll
Dienen in derWirthschaft,dievereintwir imPacht-hof neu beginnen, wie's der
tell you. Lestthe farm fall in neglect,let a stout maid be selected; 'twas our

Lionel.
P.
L.
Mutter Wil-le meint. Se-gen, ja Se-gen ih-rem An-ge-
dying mother's will. Bless-ed, oh bless-ed be her gen-tle
Plunkett.
L.
P.
den-ken. Ja, sie war ein bra-ves Weib, wuss-te Al-les recht zu
mem'ry. She was good as she was kind, Taught us both law and o-
P.
len-ken, hielt uns gut an Seel' und Leib. Dir, dem Pfleg-ling, ward die
be-dience, ne'er her e-qual we shall find. You, her fos-ter-child and
Vl.
colla voce
Cello
P.
Pfle-ge, Dei-nem from-men Sinn zum Lohn; ich, der Töl-pel, krieg-te
fav'rite, you were spar'd of life the rough, I, the clum-sy bear and
Lionel.
Plunkett.
P.
L.
Schlä-ge, na, ich war der eig'-ne Sohn! Gu-ter Bruder! Was ist's wei-ter? Ständest
blockhead, 'tho her son, got all the cuffs! Ah, my brother! Well, no mat-ter, you I
Hns.& Bssn. sustain

P.
sonst ja ganz al-lein, oh-ne El-tern, Freund, Ge-lei-ter; musst'ich
nev-er will de-sert; Friend-less or-phan, un-pro-tect-ed, you I'll
Str.
nicht dein Bru-der sein, musst'ich nicht dein Bru-der sein?
aid with hand and heart, you I'll aid with hand and heart.
Ob.
p Wood
ff Tutti
f
Larghetto.
Cl.
p
Hns. & Bssn.
Fl. & Picc.
Ob. & Cl.
ff Tutti p Str.
L.
Lionel.
Ja, seit frü-her Kind-heit Ta-gen, wart Ihr des Ver-
When to life I woke and sor-row, 'Neath your roof I
lass'-nen Heil, lehr-tet ihn das Da-sein tra-gen, gabt ihm Eu-er
found a home, Peaceful glid-ed ev-'ry mor-row, Ne'er from you my

L.
Her-zen Theil. Dei-ner bra-ven El-tern Hüt-te naht' mein Va-ter
heart can roam. By my fa-ther's hand con-fid-ed, You re-ceiv'd the
Cl.
L.
einst ver-bannt; er fand Schutz in Eu-rer Mit-te, ach, und
ex-ile's trust; In your midst he long a-bid-ed, Ye to
ad lib.
L.
starb dort un-be-kannt, ja, er starb dort un-be-kannt.
earth con-sign'd his dust, ye to earth consign'd his dust.
Wind
Str.
f Tutti
Cl
p
Hns. & Bssn.
Fl. & Picc.
Ob. & Cl.
f Tutti
Plunkett.
P.
Nim-mer ha-ben wir er-fah-ren sei-nen Na-men, sei-nen Stand,
Yes a-mongst us he did lin-ger, Ne'er re-veal'd his rank or name;
Ob.
p Cl. Hns. & Bssn.

P.
nur den Ring dort, zu be-wah-ren, zog er fest an dei-ne Hand.
Dy-ing, plac'd up-on thy fin-ger, Yon-der ring of jew-ell'd flame.
Cl.
Ob.
Dräu-en, sprach er, dir Ge-fah-ren, zei-ge ihn der Kö-ni-
"Should a dan-ger e'er come nigh thee, Send it straightway to the
Str.
gin, und sie wird dein Recht dir wahren; doch in Drangsal nur zieh'
Queen, Let it till that hour be nigh thee, She will know what it doth
Wind.
Str.
Lionel.
hin, ja, in Drang-sal nur zieh' hin. Denn so
mean, she will know what it doth mean." Ne'er hath
colla voce
Fl. Ob. & Cl.
Str.
L.
lang' du, froh, zu-frie-den, wei-lest in der De-muth Schoos,
world-ly pomp al-lur'd me; With my peace-ful lot con-tent,

stre-be nie_ nach Glanz hie-nie-den, Glück wohnt nur im schlich-ten Loos.
All my hum-ble wants as-sur'd me, My un-trou-bled day are spent.
Lionel.
L.
Ja, ge-hei-ligt sei_ sein Wil-le, nicht nach Schimmer strebt mein Sinn,
Yes, my fa-ther's will shall guide us, Calm and blame-less be_ our days,
Plunkett.
P.
Ja, ge-hei-ligt sei_ sein Wil-le, nicht nach Schimmer strebt sein Sinn,
Yes, thy fa-ther's will shall guide us, Calm and blame-less be our days,
Cl.
L.
und in länd-lich frommer Stil-le hei-ter fliess' mein Le-ben hin,
When the storms of fate have tried us, Ours the love, that ne'er be-trays,
P.
und in länd-lich frommer Stil-le hei-ter fliess' sein Le-ben hin,
When the storms of fate have tried us, Ours the love, that ne'er be-trays,
L.
hei-ter fliess' mein Le-ben hin.
ours the love, that ne'er be-trays.
P.
hei-ter fliess' sein Le-ben hin.
ours the love, that ne'er be-trays.
Wind
Str.
f
Tutti

Nº 6. Finale.—„Der Markt beginnt! Die Glocke schallt!"

Flute, Piccolo, Oboes, Clarinets in B flat, Bassoons, Horns in F and B flat, Trumpets in B flat, Trombone and Ophicleide, Kettle-drums in F and B flat, Big Drum and Strings.

Allegro. (bells are heard ringing)
f Tutti
f Chorus of Servantmaids.
Der Markt be-ginnt! Die Glo - cke schallt! Der Richter naht mit Amts-ge-walt. Her-bei! Ihr
The fair be-gins with sound of bell, The Sheriff comes, now mark him well. Ye maids, come
Der Markt be-ginnt! Die Glo - cke schallt! Der Richter naht mit Amts-ge-walt. Her-bei! Ihr
The fair be-gins with sound of bell, The Sheriff comes, now mark him well. Ye maids, come
Der Markt be-ginnt! Die Glo - cke schallt! Der Richter naht mit Amts-ge-walt.
The fair be-gins with sound of bell, The Sheriff comes, now mark him well.
f Farmers' Wives.
Der Markt be-ginnt! Die Glo - cke schallt! Der Richter naht mit Amts-ge-walt. Her-bei! Ihr
The fair be-gins with sound of bell, The Sheriff comes, now mark him well. Ye maids, come
f Chorus of Farmers.
Der Markt be-ginnt! Die Glo - cke schallt! Der Richter naht mit Amts-ge-walt. Her-bei! Ihr
The fair be-gins with sound of bell, The Sheriff comes, now mark him well. Ye maids, come
Der Markt be-ginnt! Die Glo - cke schallt! Der Richter naht mit Amts-ge-walt.
The fair be-gins with sound of bell, The Sheriff comes, now mark him well.
Cl.
f Str. Hns. & Bssn.

Mäg-de, jung und alt, her-bei, her - bei, her-bei!
forth, both old and young, come forth, come forth, come forth!
Mäg-de, jung und alt, her-bei, her - bei, her-bei!
forth, both old and young, come forth, come forth, come forth!
Mäg-de, jung und alt, her-bei, her - bei, her-bei!
forth, both old and young, come forth, come forth, come forth!
Mäg-de, jung und alt, her-bei, her - bei, her-bei!
forth, both old and young, come forth, come forth, come forth!
ff Tutti
Sheriff.
Sh.
Raum und Platz der O-brigkeit! (Leu-te, macht euch nicht so breit!)
All make way here for the law! (Such a crowd I nev-er saw!)
Raum und Platz der O-brig-
All make way here for the
Raum und Platz der O-brig-
All make way here for the
Raum und Platz der O-brig-
All make way here for the
Raum und Platz der O-brig-
All make way here for the
f Str.
p Wind
f Tutti

Hört! Was das Ge - setz euch spricht! Hö-ret! A - ber stört mich nicht!
I the statute first will read, Then to bus'ness we'll pro - ceed.
keit!
law!
Hö - ret!
Neighbors,
f Str.
p Wind
f Tutti
Sheriff (reads).
„An - na! Wir von Got - tes Gna - den" Hut ab!
"Tis our roy - al will and plea - sure!" Hats off!
A - ber stört ihn nicht!
let us hear him read.
p Brass
p Str. pizz.

Sh.
Schlingels, so wie ich! Höf-lichkeit kann nimmer schaden! „Wir er - ken-nen feier-lich
Rustics, look at me! Loy-al feel-ings let us cherish. "We, Queen Anne, here-by de-cree
Brass
Sh.
Richmonds Pri-vi - le-gi - a si-gil-la-ta re-gi - a, dass die Magd, die sich dem
to all subjects of the crown, dwelling here in Richmond town, Who-so at the fair en -
pp Str. arco
p Wind Str. pizz.
Sh.
Mie-ther hier auf off - nem Markt ver - dingt, für ein Jahr bei
gag-es To per - form a ser - vant's part, For a year her
Sh.
dem Ge - bie - ter wei - len muss, wenn er's be - dingt,
ser - vice pledg-es; From this law, let none de - part.
Sh.
oh - ne Wei-gern und Ent - kommen, ward das Handgeld an - ge - nom-men!"
When the ear-nest - mon-ey's ta-ken, Let the bar-gain stay un - sha-ken."
Ob.
Bssn.
Str.

Chorus.
Sheriff.
Habt's ca-pirt? Schon lan-ge, schon lan-ge! Schön! Auf, ihr Dirnen_lasst euch
Ye have heard. We have, sir, we have, sir! Good! Now, my lasses, state your
Schon lan-ge, schon lan-ge!
We have, sir, we have, sir!
f Tutti
seh'n!
case.
Animato.
Wind sustain
Allegretto.
First Servant.
Sprich! Was kannst du, Mol-ly Pitt? Ich kann nä-hen, ich kann mä-hen, ich kann
What can you do, Mol-ly Pitt? I can sow, sir, I can mow, sir, I can
Fl. & Vl.
p Str.
sä-en, Fä-den dre-hen, ich kann bügeln, ich kannstriegelnund ver-se-hen Hof und
bake and brew, Mend things like new, Can mind a house, and rule it too, There's naught I can-not

Sheriff.
A Farmer.
I.S.
Sh.
F.
Haus! Vier Gui - ne - en! Wer ist Bie - ter? Kann ge-sche-hen! Ich bin Mie-ther.
do! Worth four guin-eas! who will hire her? On my farm I shall re-quire her.
Tutti
Sheriff.
Second Servant.
Sh.
II.S.
Sag, was kannst du, Pol - ly Smitt? Ich kann stricken, Ich kann sti - cken, Braten
What can you do, Pol - ly Smith? I can cook, sir, By the book, sir, I can
Fl. &Vl.
Str.
II.S.
spi - cken! Klei - der fli - cken, Rö - cke klo - pfen, Gän - se stop - fen, Por - ter pfropfen, wie der
roast and toast, And 'tis my boast That no - thing in a house that I preside in yet was
Sheriff.
Farmer's Wife.
II.S.
Sh.
F.W.
Daus! Fünf Gui - ne - en! Wer will's wagen? Sei's da - rum. Topp! Zu - ge - schlagen!
lost. Worth five guin-eas! who will venture? Done for me, she's free from censure!
Tutti
Sheriff.
Third Servant.
Sh.
III.S.
Und was leis - tet Bet - si Witt? Ich kann scheu - ern, Bro - de säu - ern, ich kann
Well, what say'st thou, Bet - sy White? I can churn, sir, To a turn, sir, I can
Fl. &Vl.
Str.

mästen, Beefsteak rös-ten, has-peln, ras-peln, glät-ten, plät-ten, stopf' die Bet-ten weich und
fry and grill, And mind the mill, I'm one that nev-er can sit still, All or.-ders I__ ful-
Sheriff.
kraus. Kit-ty Bell, und Lid-dy Well, und Nel-ly Box, und Sal-ly Fox!
fil. Kit-ty Bell, and Lid-dy Well, and Nel-ly Box, and Sal-ly Fox!
p Str.
Str. & Wood
Four Servants.
Ich kann ba-cken, ich kann bra-ten, gra-ben, ha-cken mit dem
I can dig well, Cure a pig well, I can see no harm Comes
Spa-ten, ich kann spinnen fei-nes Lin-nen und ge-win-nen Geld für's
to your farm! For ev-'ry ill I know a charm, All er.-rors I__ re-
Four Servants.
Ich kann stri-cken, ich kann sti-cken, Braten spi-cken, Klei-der
I can sow, sir, I can mow, sir, I can bake and brew, mend
Haus! ich kann backen, ich kann braten, graben, ha-cken
form! Two Servants. I can cook, sir, by the book, sir, I can roast and
Ich kann scheuern, ich kann säuern, ich kann mästen, Beefsteak rös-ten,
I can churn, sir, to a turn, sir, I've a master'y too in pas-try,

fli - cken, Rö - cke klopfen, Gänse stopfen, Por - ter pfropfen, wie der Daus! Ich kann
things like new, I'll mind a house and rule it too, there's naught I can-not do. I'm a
mit dem Spa-ten, ich kann spinnen fei - nes Lin-nen und ge-win - nen Geld für's Haus.
toast, and 'tis my boast that nothing in a house that I preside in yet was lost.
haspeln, raspeln, glät-ten, plät-ten, stopf' die Bet-ten weich und kraus, ja, weich und kraus.
I can fry and grill and mind the mill, and all your or-ders I at once ful - fil.
f
Kin-der he - gen, pfle - gen, wie - gen, hü - ten, wie - gen, hü - ten, ich kann Kin-der he - gen,
splendid nurse for ba - bies, With no in - ter-fer - ing la - dies, I'm a splendid nurse for
Ich lass Tau - ben, Gän - se, En - ten, Hüh-ner brü - ten, ich lass
I know how to make the hens lay all the win - ter, I know
Und ich dien-te gar zu gern
Geese and hens I un - der - stand,
pfle - gen, wie - gen, hü - ten, wiegen, hü - ten, und ich diente gar zu gern bei 'nem al - ten, wa-ckern
babies, With no in - ter-fer-ing la - dies; If a widow-er ap - pears, Rich in purse and old in
Tauben, Gän-se, En - ten, Hühner brü - ten, und ich diente gar zu gern bei 'nem
how to make the hens lay all the win-ter; If a widow-er ap - pears, Rich in
bei 'nem al - ten, wackern Herrn! Auch ein Wit-wer dürft' es
Like no damsel in the land. If a widow - er ap -

Herrn!
years,
Auch ein Wit-wer dürft' es sein, wo ich wä-re ganz al-
Him I'll serve with willing heart, Nor from him will ev-er
al-ten, wa-ckern Herrn, ja, bei 'nem al-ten, wackern, al-ten, wackern Herrn, wo ich wä-re ganz al-
purse and old in years, Oh, him I'll serve with willing heart, with willing heart, Nor from him will ev-er
sein, ja, auch ein Wit-wer dürft' es sein, ja, auch ein Wit-wer dürft' es sein, wo ich wä-re ganz al-
pears Who's rich in purse and old in years, Oh, him I'll serve with willing heart, Nor from him will ev-er
Sheriff.
Sh.
Halt! Mit Ver-laub! Ihr macht mich taub, ihr macht mich taub, ihr macht mich
No more, good lasses, by your leave, Pray from this din my ears re-
lein, wo ich wä-re ganz al-lein, wo ich wä-re ganz al-
part, nor from him will ev-er part, no, from him I'll nev-er
lein, wo ich wä-re ganz al-lein, wo ich wä-re ganz al-
part, nor from him will ev-er part, no, from him I'll nev-er
lein, wo ich wä-re ganz al-lein, wo ich wä-re ganz al-
part, nor from him will ev-er part, no, from him I'll nev-er
Tutti
Sh.
taub, halt, mit Ver-laub, ihr macht mich taub!
lieve, pray from this din my ears re-lieve!
lein. Ich kann nä-hen, ich kann mähen, ich kann sä-en, Fä-den
part. I can sow, sir, I can mow, sir, I can bake and brew, mend
lein. Ich kann stricken, ich kann sticken, Braten spi-cken, Klei-der
part. I can roast and toast, and 'tis my boast that where I am no-
lein. Ich kann scheuern, Brode säuern, ich kann mäs-ten, Beefsteak
part. I can churn, sir, to a turn, sir, I can fry and grill and
f Wind

dre-hen, ich kann nä-hen, ich kann mä-hen, ich kann sä-en, Fä-den dre-hen, ich kann
things like new, I mow, I sow, I bake, I brew, I mend your things to look like new, I
fli-cken, ich kann stri-cken, ich kann sti-cken, Braten spi-cken, Klei-der fli-cken, Rö-cke
thing is lost, I roast, I toast, I cook by book, I roast and toast, and 'tis my boast that
rös-ten, ich kann scheuern, Bro-de säu-ern, ich kann mästen, Beefsteak rösten, haspeln,
mind the mill, I churn, I turn, I fry, I grill, I can if need be mind the mill, I'm
ff
Wol-len se-hen, wie sie nä-hen, wie sie mä-hen, Fä-den drehen,
Let us see then, and a-gree then, how you sow and mow, and darn, and
ff
Wol-len se-hen, wie sie mähen, wie sie nä-hen, Fä-den dre-hen, wie sie
Let us see then, and a-gree then, how you sow and mow, and darn, and churn, and
ff
Wol-len se-hen, wie sie mähen, wie sie nä-hen, Fä-den dre-hen, wie sie
Let us see then, and a-gree then, how you sow and mow, and darn, and churn, and
ff Tutti
bü-geln, ich kann striegeln und ver-se-hen Hof und Haus, ich kann nä-hen, ich kann
mind the house and rule it, too, there's naught I can-not do, I can sow, sir, I can
klopfen, Gän-se stopfen, Por-ter pfropfen, wie der Daus, ich kann stricken, ich kann
nothing in a house that I pre-side in yet was lost, I can cook, sir, by the
raspeln, glät-ten, plät-ten, stopf' die Bet-ten weich und kraus, ich kann scheuern, Bro-de
one that never can sit still, all or-ders I ful-fil, I can churn, sir, to a
wie sie bü-geln, wie sie striegeln und ver-se-hen Hof und Haus, wollen se-hen,
churn, and if your work's done to a turn, good wa-ges you shall earn, let us see then,
bü-geln, wie sie striegeln und ver-se-hen Hof und Haus, wollen se-hen, wie sie
if your work's done to a turn, good wa-ges you shall earn, let us see then, and a-
bü-geln, wie sie striegeln und ver-se-hen Hof und Haus, wollen se-hen, wie sie
if your work's done to a turn, good wa-ges you shall earn, let us see then, and a-

mä-hen, ich kann sä-en, Fä-den dre-hen, ich kann bü-geln, ich kann strie-geln und ver-
mow, sir, I can bake and brew, mend things like new, I mow, I sow, I bake, I brew, I
sticken, Bra-ten spicken, Klei-der fli-cken, Röcke klopfen, Gän-se stopfen, Por-ter
book, sir, I can roast and toast, and 'tis my boast that nothing in a house that I pre-
säu-ern, ich kann mästen, Beefsteak rösten, haspeln, raspeln, glät-ten, plät-ten, stopf' die
turn, sir, I can fry and grill, and mind the mill, I'm one that nev-er can sit still, all
wie sie nä-hen, wie sie mä-hen, Fä-den dre-hen, wie sie bü-geln, wie sie striegeln
and a-gree then, how you sow and mow, and darn and churn, and if your work's done to a
nä-hen, wie sie mähen, Fä-den dre-hen, wie sie bü-geln, wie sie strie-geln und ver-
gree then, how you sow and mow, and darn and churn, and if your work's done to a turn, good
nä-hen, wie sie mähen, Fä-den dre-hen, wie sie bü-geln, wie sie strie-geln und ver-
gree then, how you sow and mow, and darn and churn, and if your work's done to a turn, good
se-hen Hof und Haus, ich kann nä-hen, ich kann mä-hen, ich kann sä-en, Fä-den
mend your things like new, I can sow and mow, and bake and brew, I mend your things to
pfropfen, wie der Daus, ich kann stricken, ich kann sti-cken, Bra-ten spi-cken, Kleider
side in yet was lost, I can cook by book, and roast and toast, and 'tis my boast that
Bet-ten weich und kraus, ich kann scheuern, Bro-de säu-ern, ich kann mästen, Beefsteak
or-ders I ful-fil, I can churn and turn, and fry and grill, I can if need be
und ver-se-hen Hof und Haus, wol-len se-hen, wie sie nä-hen, wie sie mä-hen,
turn, good wa-ges you shall earn, let us see then, and a-gree then, how you sow and
se-hen Hof und Haus, wol-len se-hen, wie sie nä-hen, wie sie mä-hen,
wa-ges you shall earn, let us see then, and a-gree then, how you sow and
se-hen Hof und Haus, wol-len se-hen, wie sie nä-hen, wie sie mähen, Fä-den
wa-ges you shall earn, let us see then, and a-gree then, how you sow and mow, and

dre-hen, ich kann bü-geln, ich kann strie-geln, und ver-se-hen Hof und Haus, ja, Hof und
look like new, I mind the house and rule it, too, there's naught, no, there is naught I can-not
fli-cken, Rö-cke klop-fen, Gän-se stop-fen, Por-ter pfrop-fen, wie der Daus, ja wie der
nothing in a house that I pre-side in yet was lost, no, no-thing yet with me was
rös-ten, haspeln, rasp-eln, glät-ten, plät-ten, stopf' die Bet-ten weich und kraus, ja, weich und
mind the mill, I'm one that nev-er can sit still, all or-ders, yes, all or-ders I ful-
Fä-den dre-hen, wie sie bü-geln, wie sie strie-geln und ver-se-hen Hof, ja, Hof und
mow, and darn and churn and if your work's done to a turn, good wa-ges you from us shall
Fä-den dre-hen, wie sie bü-geln, wie sie strie-geln und ver-se-hen Hof, ja, Hof und
mow, and darn and churn and if your work's done to a turn, good wa-ges you from us shall
dre-hen, wie sie bü-geln, wie sie strie-geln und ver-se-hen Hof und Haus!
darn and churn and if your work's done to a turn, good wa-ges you shall earn!
Haus! Topp! Herr, es gilt der Kauf!
do! Done! so the bar-gain's made!
Daus! Topp! Herr, es gilt der Kauf!
lost! Done! so the bar-gain's made!
kraus! Topp! Herr, es gilt der Kauf!
fil! Done! so the bar-gain's made!
Haus! Topp! Mä-del, 's gilt der Kauf!
earn! Done! so the bar-gain's made!
Haus! Mädel, 's gilt der Kauf! Topp! hier das Handgeld d'rauf!
earn! so the bargain's made! Done! here's the mon-ey paid!
Topp! Mädel, 's gilt der Kauf! Topp! hier das Handgeld d'rauf!
Done! so the bargain's made! Done! here's the mon-ey paid!
Str. & Brass
Str. & Wood
Str. & Brass

Topp! gebt das Hand-geld d'rauf! Ich kann nä-hen, ich kann mä-hen, ich kann
Done! here's the mon-ey paid! I can sow, sir, I can mow, sir, I can
Topp! gebt das Hand-geld d'rauf! Ich kann stricken, ich kann sti-cken, Bra-ten
Done! here's the mon-ey paid! I can cook, sir, by the book, sir, I can
Topp! gebt das Hand-geld d'rauf! Ich kann scheuern, Bro-de, säu-ern, ich kann
Done! here's the mon-ey paid! I can churn, sir, to a turn, sir, I can
Topp! gebt das Hand-geld d'rauf! Wol-len se-hen, wie sie nä-hen, wie sie
Done! here's the mon-ey paid! We will see then, and a-gree then, how you
Wol-len se-hen, wie sie nä-hen, wie sie mä-hen,
We will see then, and a-gree then, how you sow and
Wol-len se-hen, wie sie nä-hen, wie sie mä-hen,
We will see then, and a-gree then, how you sow and
Str.&Wood
Hns. sustain
sä-en, Fä-den dre-hen, ich kann bü-geln, ich kann striegeln und ver-se-hen Hof und
milk, and mind a cow, sir, I can mind a house and rule it, too, there's naught I can-not
spi-cken, Kleider fli-cken, Rö-cke klop-fen, Gän-se stop-fen, Por-ter pfropfen, wie der
roast, and toast, and 'tis my boast that no-thing in a house that I preside in yet was
mäs-ten, Beef-steak rös-ten, haspeln, ras-peln, glät-ten, plät-ten, stopf' die Bet-ten weich und
fry and grill, and mind the mill, I'm one that nev-er can sit still, all or-ders I ful-
mä-hen, Fä-den dre-hen, wie sie bü-geln, wie sie striegeln und ver-se-hen Hof und
sow and mow, and darn and churn, and if your work's done to a turn, good wages you shall
Fä-den dre-hen, wie sie bü-geln, wie sie strie-geln und ver-se-hen Hof und Haus!
mow, and darn and churn, and if your work's done to a turn, good wages you shall earn.
Fä-den dre-hen, wie sie bü-geln, wie sie strie-geln und ver-se-hen Hof und Haus!
mow, and darn and churn, and if your work's done to a turn, good wages you shall earn.
Tutti

Più animato.
Haus! Herr, es gilt der Kauf, Topp, gebt das Handgeld d'rauf, Topp, Herr, es gilt der Kauf,
do. So the bargain's made, done, here's the mon-ey paid, done, so the bargain's made,
Daus! Herr, es gilt der Kauf, Topp, gebt das Handgeld d'rauf, Topp, Herr, es gilt der Kauf,
lost. So the bar-gain's made, done, here's the mon-ey paid, done, so the bargain's made,
kraus! Herr, es gilt der Kauf, Topp, gebt das Handgeld d'rauf, Topp, Herr, es gilt der Kauf,
fil. So the bar-gain's made, done, here's the mon-ey paid, done, so the bargain's made,
Haus! Mä-del, 's gilt der Kauf, Topp, hier das Handgeld d'rauf, Topp, Mädel, 's gilt der Kauf,
earn. So the bar-gain's made, done, there's the mon-ey paid, done, so the bargain's made,
Topp, Mä-del, 's gilt der Kauf, Topp, hier das Handgeld d'rauf, Topp, Mädel, 's gilt der Kauf,
Done, so the bar-gain's made, done, there's the mon-ey paid, done, so the bargain's made,
Topp, Mä-del, 's gilt der Kauf, Topp, hier das Handgeld d'rauf, Topp, Mädel, 's gilt der Kauf,
Done, so the bar-gain's made, done, there's the mon-ey paid, done, so the bargain's made,
Più animato.
ff
Topp, gebt das Handgeld d'rauf, Topp, Herr, es gilt der Kauf, Topp, gebt das Handgeld d'rauf,
done, here's the mon-ey paid, done, so the bargain's made, done, here's the mon-ey paid,
Topp, gebt das Handgeld d'rauf, Topp, Herr, es gilt der Kauf, Topp, gebt das Handgeld d'rauf,
done, here's the mon-ey paid, done, so the bargain's made, done, here's the mon-ey paid,
Topp, gebt das Handgeld d'rauf, Topp, Herr, es gilt der Kauf, Topp, gebt das Handgeld d'rauf,
done, here's the mon-ey paid, done, so the bargain's made, done, here's the mon-ey paid,
Topp, hier das Handgeld d'rauf, Topp, Mä-del, 's gilt der Kauf, Topp, hier das Handgeld d'rauf,
done, there's the mon-ey paid, done, so the bargain's made, done, there's the mon-ey paid,
Topp, hier das Handgeld d'rauf, Topp, Mä-del, 's gilt der Kauf, Topp, hier das Handgeld d'rauf,
done, there's the mon-ey paid, done, so the bargain's made, done, there's the mon-ey paid,
Topp, hier das Handgeld d'rauf, Topp, Mä-del, 's gilt der Kauf, Topp, hier das Handgeld d'rauf,
done, there's the mon-ey paid, done, so the bargain's made, done, there's the mon-ey paid,

Topp, Herr, es gilt der Kauf, Topp, gebt das Hand - geld d'rauf,
done, so the bar-gain's made, done, here's the mon - ey paid,
Topp, Herr, es gilt der Kauf, Topp, gebt das Hand - geld d'rauf,
done, so the bar-gain's made, done, here's the mon - ey paid,
Topp, Herr, es gilt der Kauf, Topp, gebt das Hand - geld d'rauf,
done, so the bar-gain's made, done, here's the mon - ey paid,
Topp, Mä - del, 's gilt der Kauf, Topp, hier das Hand - geld d'rauf, Mä - del,
done, so the bar-gain's made, done, there's the mon - ey paid, so the
Topp, Mä - del, 's gilt der Kauf, Topp, hier das Hand - geld d'rauf, Mä - del,
done, so the bar-gain's made, done, there's the mon - ey paid, so the
Topp, Mä - del, 's gilt der Kauf, Topp, hier das Hand - geld d'rauf, Mä - del,
done, so the bar-gain's made, done, there's the mon - ey paid, so the
es gilt der Kauf, es gilt der Kauf, es gilt der Kauf, das Handgeld
the bar-gain's made, the money's paid, the bar - gain's made, the mon-ey
es gilt der Kauf, es gilt der Kauf, es gilt der Kauf, das Handgeld
the bar-gain's made, the money's paid, the bar - gain's made, the mon-ey
es gilt der Kauf, es gilt der Kauf, es gilt der Kauf, das Handgeld
the bar-gain's made, the money's paid, the bar - gain's made, the mon-ey
'sgilt der Kauf, hier das Hand-geld d'rauf, es gilt der Kauf, das Handgeld
bar - gain's made, there's the mon - ey paid, the bar-gain's made, the mon-ey
'sgilt der Kauf, hier das Hand-geld d'rauf, es gilt der Kauf, das Handgeld
bar - gain's made, there's the mon - ey paid, the bar-gain's made, the mon-ey
'sgilt der Kauf, hier das Hand-geld d'rauf, es gilt der Kauf, das Handgeld
bar - gain's made, there's the mon - ey paid, the bar-gain's made, the mon-ey

d'rauf, es gilt der Kauf, das Handgeld d'rauf!
paid, the bar-gain's made, the mon-ey paid!
d'rauf, es gilt der Kauf, das Handgeld d'rauf!
paid, the bar-gain's made, the mon-ey paid!
d'rauf, es gilt der Kauf, das Handgeld d'rauf!
paid, the bar-gain's made, the mon-ey paid!
d'rauf, es gilt der Kauf, das Handgeld d'rauf!
paid, the bar-gain's made, the mon-ey paid!
d'rauf, es gilt der Kauf, das Handgeld d'rauf!
paid, the bar-gain's made, the mon-ey paid!
d'rauf, es gilt der Kauf, das Handgeld d'rauf!
paid, the bar-gain's made, the mon-ey paid!
ff
(They crowd round the Sheriff, so that the front of the stage remains clear.)

Andante. (Enter Lady Harriet and Nancy in peasant costumes, with Sir Tristram.)
Picc. & Ob.
p
Cl. & Vl. pizz.
Lady H. Allegretto.
H.
Vorwärts, Bob,
This way, Rob,
Str. arco
H.
N.
T.
Nancy.
Tristram.
muss man Euch zie-hen? Bob! mein Freund, schaut nicht so gram. Bob! O
what, must I lead you? Come, good Rob, now be a-wake. Rob! O
T.
pfui! könnt' ich nur flie-hen o ich ar-mes Op-fer-lamm!
fie! why did I heed you? I'm a lamb led to the stake.
Lady H.
H.
O wie freundlich, o wie hei-ter Al-les un-serm Blick er-scheint!
How di-vert-ing, how a-mus-ing, all up-on us seem to smile!
Nancy.
N.
O wie freundlich, o wie hei-ter Al-les un-serm Blick er-scheint!
How di-vert-ing, how a-mus-ing, all up-on us seem to smile!
Tristram.
T.
Kö-nig-li-cher Pa-gen-lei-ter! Herz, er-star-re! Au-gen, weint!
My po-si-tion's most con-fus-ing! I'm en-trapp'd by wo-man's wile.
p Str.
Wind
Tutti
f

Recit.
Plunkett.
Lionel.
Plunkett.
Wet-ter! Ein Paar schmucke Kinder! In der That, wie zart und fein! Fast zu zart für Stall und
Broth-er! look, what pretty lasses! Yes in-deed, a charming pair. Theirs are not like servant's
p Str.
Lionel.
Plunkett.
Tristram.
Rinder_ Doch für's Haus! Ja! das mag sein.
fac-es_ Let's en-quire! Ask who they are.
Wie die Bau-ern Euch be-
How these rustics both are
Ob.
a tempo
Vla. & Cello
Lady H.
Wo denkt ihr hin?
What would ye do?
Nancy.
Tristram.
gaf-fen,_ fort von hier_ Wo denkt ihr hin? Hab' mit Plebs nicht gern zu
staring_ let us fly_ What would ye do? With the mob I'm not for-
Bssn.
Nein, nein, nein! Will als Die-ne-rin mich bei Euch nun nicht ver-
No, no, no! In the o-pen fair I re-fuse you for my
Nancy.
Nein, nein, nein!
No, no, no!
Tristram.
schaffen_ Fort! fort, fort!
bearing_ come! let's go.
f p Str.
Tutti

din-gen.
master.
Ei! Ihr könnt sie doch nicht zwingen, Pächter Bob, wenn sie nicht
Well! at least you can-not force her, master Rob, against her
Al-bernhei-ten! Schweigt doch still!
Non-sense, nonsense, pray be still!
Ja, wenn ich nun doch nicht will,
Nay, my wish you must ful-fil,
ja, wenn ich nun durch-aus nicht
you can-not force me 'gainst my
will?
will!
Pächter Bob, wenn sie nicht
Master Rob, not 'gainst her
Lionel.
Ja, wenn sie nun durch-aus nicht
Pray do not force her 'gainst her
Plunkett.
Ja, wenn das Mädel nun nicht will, wenn das Mä-del nun nicht
Don't force the girl against her will do not force her 'gainst her
will, wenn ich nicht will, wenn ich nicht will!
will, against my will, a-gainst my will!
will, wenn sie nicht will, wenn sie nicht will!
will, not 'gainst her will, not 'gainst her will!
will, wenn sie nicht will, wenn sie nicht will!
will, not 'gainst her will, not 'gainst her will!
will, wenn sie nicht will, wenn sie nicht will! 'S gibt der Mädel ja noch mehr! He! ihr dorten! kommt doch
will, against her will, a-gainst her will! There are servants and to spare! come, ye lasses, here re-
Tutti

H.
N.
T.
P.
L.
Un-ver - gleichlich!
How he ra-ges!
Un-ver - gleichlich!
How he ra-ges!
Tristram.
Un-er-hö-ret!
Vulgar wretches!
her! Hier ein Miether der zahlt reichlich!
pair. Come and hire for goodly wages.
Chorus (crowding round Sir Tristram).
SOPR. Ich kann nä-hen, ich kann
I can sow, sir, I can
ALTO.
Ob. Hns. & Tromb.
Lady H.
O wie munter, o wie hei-ter, immer
Oh how mer-ry, how de-light-ful, and I
Nancy.
O wie mun-ter, o wie
Oh how mer-ry, how de -
Tristram.
Ha! Ab - scheulich, gräss - lich,
This is fright-ful, she is
Lionel.
Die kann nä-hen, die kann
She can sow, sir, she can
Plunkett.
Die kann nä-hen, die kann
She can sow, sir, she can
mä-hen, ich kann sä-en, Fä-den dre-hen, ich kann nä-hen, ich kann mä-hen, ich kann
mow, sir, I can milk and mind a cow, sir, I can sow, sir, I can mow, sir, I can
8
Str. & Wind

bun-ter geht es wei-ter, wie sie zwängen ihn und en-gen; ha, sie drän-gen ihn hin-
feel a lit-tle spiteful, For his cautious ways are fright-ful, And to-day I will be-
hei-ter, im- -mer bun-ter geht es wei-ter,
lightful, his pre-ten-sions make me spite-ful,
gräulich! Un- ver-zeihlich! Wie ent-eil' ich?
spiteful! I up-held but what was rightful,
mä-hen, die kann sä-en, Fä- den dre-hen,
mow, sir, she can i-ron, bake and brew, sir,
mä-hen, die kann sä-en, Fä- den dre-hen,
mow, sir, she can i-ron, bake and brew, sir,
sä-en, Fä-den dre-hen, ich kann bü-geln, ich kann strie-geln und ver-se-hen Hof und
mind and milk a cow, sir, I can bake and brew, mend things like new, there's naught I can-not
aus! O wie mun-ter, o wie hei-ter, im-mer bun-ter geht es
free! Oh how mer-ry, how de-light-ful, And I feel a lit-tle
wie sie zwän-gen ihn und en-gen,
He's a pe-dant old and frightful,
Nichts ist hei-lig ih- -ren Gril-len,
How es- cape them? De- vil take them!
die kann bü-geln, die kann striegeln,
Say, what would you have her do, sir?
die kann bü-geln, die kann striegeln,
Say, what would you have her do, sir?
Haus, und ich kann stri-cken, ich kann sti-cken, Bra-ten spicken, Klei-der
do, and I can cook, sir, by the book, sir, I can roast and toast, and

H.
wei-ter, wie sie zwän-gen ihn und en-gen, ha, sie drän-gen ihn hin-
spite-ful, For his cau-tious ways are frightful, And to-day I will be
N.
ha, sie drän-gen ihn hin-aus, ihn hin-
Till to-mor-row we'll be free, we'll be
T.
ih-rem Wil-len Fort! hin-aus, fort hin-
they will mis-chief bring on her, bring on
L.
die pfropft Por-ter wie der Daus, wie der
one to choose, sir, you are free, you are
P.
die pfropft Por-ter wie der Daus, wie der
one to choose, sir, you are free, you are
fli-cken, Rö-cke klop-fen, Gän-se stop-fen, Por-ter pfrop-fen, wie der
'tis my boast that no-thing in a house that I pre-side in, yet was
aus, sie drän-gen ihn hin-aus!
free! To-day I will be free!
aus, sie drän-gen ihn hin-aus!
free, to-day we will be free!
aus!
her!
Daus! ja, sie drän-gen ihn hin-aus! ha, sie drän-gen ihn hin-aus!
free, one to choose, sir, you are free, one to choose, sir, you are free!
Daus! ja, sie drän-gen ihn hin-aus! ha, sie drän-gen ihn hin-aus!
free, one to choose, sir, you are free, one to choose, sir, you are free!
Daus, und ich kann scheuern, Bro-de säu-ern, ich kann mäs-ten, Beef-steak rös-ten,
lost, and I can churn, sir, to a turn, sir, I can fry and grill and mind the

ff
Wie sie zwän-gen ihn und en-gen, ha! sie drän-gen ihn hin-
How they seize him, how they tease him, From their taunts he can-not
has-peln, ras-peln, glät-ten, plät-ten, stopf' die Bet-ten weich und
mill, I'm one that nev-er can sit still, all or-ders I'll ful-
f Tutti
Lady H.
ha, sie drän-gen ihn hin-aus!
Nancy. From their taunts he can-not flee!
aus, ha, sie drän-gen ihn hin-aus!
flee, from their taunts he can-not flee!
kraus, stopf' die Bet-ten weich und kraus, ja, weich und kraus!
fil, all your or-ders, all your or-ders I'll ful-fil!

„Sieh' nur, wie sie uns betrachten!"

Lionel.
Plunkett.
(very much embarrassed)
Ich wag' es nicht! Ha-sen-fuss! Sollst mich'mal se-hen! Al-so_
I do not dare! Oh, pol-troon! Then I must show you! Now then_
Ob. & Fl.
Vla. & 'Cello
Str.
Wind
Nancy.
Lady H.
al-so_ Hm! Auch der bleibt stumm, der bleibt stumm! Ei! So kommt! Ja! Lass uns
now then_ Hm! This he-ro, too, has no tongue! Come a-way! I'll stay no
p Str.
cresc.
Lionel (to Plunkett).
ge-hen! Freund, sie ge-hen! Hm, hm, hm!
lon-ger. See, they leave us! Hm, hm, hm!
Plunkett.
(approaching the Ladies)
Das wär' dumm! Hm, hm, hm!
I'm struck dumb! Hm, hm, hm!
f
fz
Lady H.
Nun für-wahr! für-wahr! das lass' ich gel-ten, froh er-reicht, ja, froh er-reicht wär'
Swains so shy at court are not the fash-ion, Nev-er_ yet, ne'er yet I saw the
Nancy.
Nun für-wahr! für-wahr! das lass' ich gel-ten, froh er-reicht, ja, froh er-reicht wär'
Swains so shy at court are not the fash-ion, Nev-er_ yet, ne'er yet I saw the
Lionel.
Oh! für-wahr! für-wahr! wohl sah ich sel-ten Ei-ne, die beim er-sten Blick mir
I ne'er saw two maids of humble sta-tion, Who for grace and beau-ty could com-
Plunkett.
Oh! für-wahr! für-wahr! wohl sah ich sel-ten Ei-ne,_ die beim er-sten Blick mir
I ne'er saw two maids of humble sta-tion, Who for_ grace and beau-ty could com-

H.
un-ser Ziel. Traun! So blö-de Schäfer sah man sel-ten, was wir wag-ten,
like of these! Was there e'er so droll a sit-u-a-tion? I be-gin to
N.
un-ser Ziel. Traun! So blö-de Schäfer sah man sel-ten, was wir wag-ten,
like of these! Was there e'er so droll a sit-u-a-tion? I be-gin to
L.
so ge-fiel! Traun! Solch her-zig Mädchen lass'ich gel-ten, sol-cher Mäg-de
pare with these! One has quite bewitch'd my in-cli-na-tion, May our plans the
P.
so ge-fiel! Traun! Solch her-zig Mädchen lass'ich gel-ten, sol-cher Mäg-de
pare with these! One has quite bewitch'd my in-cli-na-tion, May our plans the
blieb ein muntres Spiel. Froh er-
feel not quite at ease. Nev-er
f
blieb ein muntres Spiel. O! für-wahr, für-wahr! das lass' ich gel-ten, froh er-
feel not quite at ease. Swains like these at court are not the fash-ion, Nev-er
f
gibt's fürwahr nicht viel. O! für-wahr, für-wahr! wohl sah ich sel-ten Ei-ne,
pret-ty dam-sels please! I ne'er saw two maids, of humble sta-tion, Who for
f
gibt's fürwahr nicht viel. O! für-wahr, für-wahr! wohl sah ich sel-ten Ei-ne,
pret-ty dam-sels please! I ne'er saw two maids, of humble sta-tion, Who for
f Str. pizz.
rit.
a tempo
p
reicht, ja froh er-reicht wär' un-ser Ziel. Traun! So blö-de Schäfer sah man sel-ten,
yet, ne'er yet I saw a pair like these; was there e'er so droll a sit-u-a-tion?
reicht, ja froh er-reicht wär' un-ser Ziel. Traun! So blö-de Schäfer sah man sel-ten,
yet, ne'er yet I saw a pair like these; was there e'er so droll a sit-u-a-tion?
die beim er-sten Blick mir so ge-fiel. Traun! Solch her-zig Mädchen lass'ich gel-ten,
grace and beau-ty could compare with these; One has quite bewitch'd my in-cli-na-tion,
die beim er-sten Blick mir so ge-fiel. Traun! Solch her-zig Mädchen lass'ich gel-ten,
grace and beau-ty could compare with these; One has quite bewitch'd my in-cli-na-tion,
col canto
a tempo

H.
was wir wag-ten, blieb ein munt'res Spiel.
I be-gin to feel not quite at ease.
N.
was wir wag-ten, blieb ein munt'res Spiel.
I be-gin to feel not quite at ease.
L.
sol-cher Mäg-de gibt's fürwahr nicht viel.
May our plans the pret-ty dam-sels please.
P.
sol-cher Mäg-de gibt's fürwahr nicht viel. Ei! Cou-
May our plans the pret-ty dam-sels please. Well, I'll
f Tutti
Più animato.
ra-ge! Mä-dels, blei-bet! Ihr ge-fal-let uns. Schlaget
ven-ture! Damsels, lis-ten! We would hire you have you
p Str.
stacc.
ein! Wenn ihr brav die Wirt-schaft trei-bet, sollt ihr lan-ge bei uns
ears? If your floors and plat-ters glis-ten, Ye shall stay with us for
P. L. H.
Lionel.
Lady H.
sein. Ja, recht lang! Als Die-ne-rin-nen?
years. Yes, for years. What, as your servants?
Vl.
Ob. Cl. Bssn. & 'Cello

Nancy. Lionel. Plunkett.
N. L. P.
Ha, ha, ha, ha! Ihr lacht? 'Sist gut, la - chend sei-nen
Ha, ha, ha, ha! You laugh? No fear; if she does her
Lady H. Nancy. Plunkett.
P. L. N.
Lohn ge-win-nen, wenn man brav die Ar-beit thut. Ar-beit? Ar-beit? Du bist
work with laughter, she's good humor'd, that is clear. What work? What work? You are
Str.
P.
für die Gän-se, er-hältst uns Haus und Stäl-le rein!
for the farmyard, to keep the house and sta-bles clean!
p
stacc.
(to Lady H.)
Lionel.
P. L.
Du be-stellst mit Hack' und Sen-se Feld und Gar-ten. Nein, o nein!
You, my lass, shall do the cook-ing, mind the gar-den— You don't mean
Plunkett.
L. P.
Solch ein zar-tes, schwa-ches We-sen muss im Hau-se Erb-sen
that this gen-tle, ten-der crea-ture should clean sta-bles? She might
Wind sustain

P.
le - sen! Jährlich kriegt Ihr fünf-zig Kro - nen und seid flei-ssig
gar - den. Fif - ty crowns shall be your wa - ges, all is found you;
f
Str.
P.
Ihr und flink, soll Euch Sonn-tags Por-ter loh-nen _ und zu Neu-jahr Plum - pud-
to be brief: Week-days cheese and beer for sup-per, and on Sun-days, good roast-
rit.
colla voce
Lady H. (laughing).
Nancy.
P.
H.
N.
ding! Ja! _ Wer kann da wi-der-ste-hen? Ja! Wer kann da wi - der -
beef. Who'd _ re - sist this splendid of-fer? Who'd re-sist this splen-did
Cl.
Lionel.
Lady H.
Lionel.
L.
H.
Topp? Ja! Topp! Das Hand-geld d'rauf! Und nun hur-tig
Done? Yes, done! Then by the pow'rs! here's the hand-sel _
Plunkett.
Nancy.
Plunkett.
N.
P.
ste-hen? Topp? Ja! Topp! Das Hand-geld d'rauf! Und nun hur-tig
of - fer? Done? Yes, done! Then by the pow'rs! here's the hand-sel _
Vl. & Fl.
Str.

Tempo I.
H.
N.
L.
P.
Nun für - wahr, fürwahr! das lass' ich gel - ten,
Swains so shy at court are not the fash-ion,
Nun für - wahr, fürwahr! das lass' ich gel - ten,
Swains so shy at court are not the fash-ion,
macht euch auf!
you are ours!
Oh! für - wahr, fürwahr! wohl sah ich sel - ten
I ne'er saw two maids of humble sta - tion,
(they give them money)
macht euch auf!
you are ours!
Oh! für - wahr, fürwahr! wohl sah ich sel - ten
I ne'er saw two maids of humble sta - tion,
Tempo I.
f Tutti
froh er - reicht, ja, froh erreicht wär' un - ser Ziel! Traun! So blö - de Schä - fer sah man
Nev - er yet, ne'er yet I saw the like of these! Was there e'er so droll a sit - u -
froh er - reicht, ja, froh erreicht wär' un - ser Ziel! Traun! So blö - de Schä - fer sah man
Nev - er yet, ne'er yet I saw the like of these! Was there e'er so droll a sit - u -
Ei - ne, die beim er - sten Blick mir so ge - fiel! Traun! Solch her - zig Mäd - chen lass' ich
Who for grace and beauty could compare with these! One has quite bewitch'd my in - cli -
Ei - ne, die beim er - sten Blick mir so ge - fiel! Traun! Solch her - zig Mäd - chen lass' ich
Who for grace and beauty could compare with these! One has quite bewitch'd my in - cli -
sel - ten, was wir wag - ten, bleibt ein muntres Spiel.
a - tion? I be - gin to feel not quite at ease.
sel - ten, was wir wag - ten, bleibt ein muntres Spiel. Nun für - wahr, für -
a - tion? I be - gin to feel not quite at ease. Swains so shy at
gel - ten, sol - che Mäg - de gibt's fürwahr nicht viel. O für - wahr, für -
na - tion, May our plans the pret - ty dam - sels please. I ne'er saw two
gel - ten, sol - che Mäg - de gibt's fürwahr nicht viel. O für - wahr, für -
na - tion, May our plans the pret - ty dam - sels please. I ne'er saw two
f Str. pizz.

f
rit.
H.
Froh er-reicht, ja, froh er-reicht wär' un-ser Ziel.
Nev - er yet, ne'er yet I saw the like of these;
N.
wahr! das lass' ich gel-ten, froh er-reicht, ja, froh er-reicht wär' un-ser Ziel.
court are not the fash-ion, Nev - er yet, ne'er yet I saw the like of these;
L.
wahr! wohl sah ich sel - ten Ei - ne, die beim er-sten Blick mir so ge-fiel.
maids of humble sta-tion, Who for grace and beauty could compare with these;
P.
wahr! wohl sah ich sel-ten Ei - ne, die beim er-sten Blick mir so ge-fiel.
maids of humble sta-tion, Who for grace and beauty could compare with these;
col canto
a tempo
f p
Traun! So blö - de Schä-fer sah man sel-ten, was wir wag-ten, blieb ein muntres
Was there e'er so droll a sit - u - a - tion? I be - gin to feel not quite at
Traun! So blö - de Schä-fer sah man sel-ten, was wir wag-ten, blieb ein muntres
Was there e'er so droll a sit - u - a - tion? I be - gin to feel not quite at
Traun! Solch her-zig Mädchen lass' ich gel-ten, sol-cher Mäg-de gibt's fürwahr nicht
One has quite be-witch'd my in-cli-na-tion, May our plans the pret-ty dam-sels
Traun! Solch her-zig Mädchen lass' ich gel-ten, sol-cher Mäg-de gibt's fürwahr nicht
One has quite be-witch'd my in-cli-na-tion, May our plans the pret-ty dam-sels
a tempo
Spiel! O für-wahr, o für - wahr, froh er - reicht wär' das Ziel, o für-wahr, o für-
ease. It is droll, it is droll, but I feel not at ease, it is droll, it is
Spiel! O für-wahr, o für - wahr, froh er - reicht wär' das Ziel, o für-wahr, o für-
ease. It is droll, it is droll, but I feel not at ease, it is droll, it is
viel! O für-wahr, o für - wahr, froh er - reicht wär' das Ziel, o für-wahr, o für-
please. Oh my heart is be-witch'd, ne'er were maids like to these, oh my heart is be-
viel! O für-wahr, o für - wahr, froh er - reicht wär' das Ziel, o für-wahr, o für-
please. Oh my heart is be-witch'd, ne'er were maids like to these, oh my heart is be-
Str. & Wood

H.
N.
L.
P.
wahr, froh er-reicht wär' das Ziel! was wir wag-ten, blieb ein Spiel, was wir
droll, but I feel not at ease, no, I do not feel at ease, no, I
wahr, froh er-reicht wär' das Ziel! was wir wag-ten, blieb ein Spiel, was wir
droll, but I feel not at ease, no, I do not feel at ease, no, I
wahr, froh er-reicht wär' das Ziel! sol-cher Mäg-de gibt's nicht viel, sol-cher
witch'd, ne'er were maids like to these, ne'er were maidens like to these, ne'er were
wahr, froh er-reicht wär' das Ziel! sol-cher Mäg-de gibt's nicht viel, sol-cher
witch'd, ne'er were maids like to these, ne'er were maidens like to these, ne'er were
f Tutti
wag-ten, blieb ein Spiel, ja, für-wahr, das lass' ich gel-ten, froh er-reicht wär' un-ser
do not feel at ease, yes, 'tis droll, our sit-u-a-tion, but I feel not quite at
wag-ten, blieb ein Spiel, ja, für-wahr, das lass' ich gel-ten, froh er-reicht wär' un-ser
do not feel at ease, yes, 'tis droll, our sit-u-a-tion, but I feel not quite at
Mäg-de gibt's nicht viel, solch ein Mäd-chen lass' ich gel-ten, sol-cher Mäg-de gibt's nicht
maidens like to these, they've be-witch'd my in-cli-na-tion, were there ev-er maids like
Mäg-de gibt's nicht viel, solch ein Mäd-chen lass' ich gel-ten, sol-cher Mäg-de gibt's nicht
maidens like to these, they've be-witch'd my in-cli-na-tion, were there ev-er maids like
Ziel, das Ziel!
ease, at ease!
Ziel, das Ziel!
ease, at ease!
viel, nicht viel!
these, like these!
viel, nicht viel!
these, like these!
f

Allegretto.
(Enter Tristram, followed by some of the maidservants.)
f Tutti
Tristram.
Hier! Da nehmt die Abstandssumme, aber lasst mich jetzt in
Here's a pound to pay the forfeit, let me go without a-
f Str.
(perceiving the others)
Ruh'!
do.
f Tutti
Recit. Tristram.
Wie! Was
But what
Recit.
Lady H. & Nancy (going over to Tristram).
Ja! Genug!
Now good-by!
Plunkett.
(holding them back)
seh' ich? Ich verstumme! Fort, hinweg! Was willst denn Du? Das möcht' ich
means this? All so friendly? How is this? Pray, who are you? Are you de-
Str.
Lionel.
Lady H.
Das möcht' ich sehen! Unerhört! Wisst denn Schweigt! Um mich geschehen
Are we demented? Ye are ours! You took Hush! For ever I'm un-
sehen! Hand-geld nahmt Ihr!
mented? Were ye not hir'd?
f

Nancy.
H.
N.
ist's, wenn man am Hof er-fährt_ Schweigt, sonst ist ihr Ruf ver-lo-ren, kommt's der bösen Welt zu
done, if at the Court they heard_ Hush, I beg you'll never mention That to hire us was th'in-
p
Lady H.
Lionel.
a tempo
Allegro.
N.
H.
L.
Oh-ren. Fort! ja, fort! Mit nich-ten! Seid ge - mie-thet für ein
tention. Yes, let's go! Ex - cuse me! We have hir'd you for a
Tristram.
Nancy.
Plunkett.
T.
N.
P.
Kommt denn! Fort! ja, fort! Mit nichten, mit nich-ten! Seid ge - mie-thet für ein
Re-turn Yes, let's go! Ex-cuse me, ex- cuse me! We have hir'd you for a
Allegro.
p a tempo
Str.
Tristram.
T.
Un-er-hört! Ich verstumme, ich verstumme, ich verstum -
'Tis unheard! I'm struck dumb, I am astounded, I'm astound -
L.
Jahr; der Herr Richter selbst mag richten, dass der Han - del gül-tig
year; let the Sheriff judge between us, That will make the mat-ter
P.
Jahr; der Herr Richter selbst mag richten, dass der Han - del gül-tig
year; let the Sheriff judge between us, That will make the mat-ter
T.
me!
ed!
L.
war.
clear!
Sheriff.
P.
Sh.
war.
clear!
Ist das Handgeld angenommen, kann der Magd kein Weigern
If the earnest-money's taken, then the bargain can't be
ff Tutti
p Vla. Cello & Bssn.

Ist das Handgeld an-ge-nommen, kann der Magd kein Weigern frommen!
If the earn-est-money's tak-en, then the bar-gain can't be shak-en!
Sh.
frommen. Ist das Handgeld an-ge-nommen, kann der Magd kein Weigern frommen!
shak-en. If the earn-est-money's tak-en, then the bar-gain can't be shak-en!
Vl.
p Wind.
cresc.
ff Tutti
Nancy.
p poco rit.
a tempo
Darf der Magd kein Weigern from-men!
No, the bar-gain can't be sha-ken!
Lionel.
Sheriff.
Plunkett.
Chorus.
f
Kein Ent - rinnen ist von hin-nen zu ge-
You are caught now, and you ought now To be
Str. pizz.
p poco rit.
f a tempo
Tutti
Str. arco
f

win-nen und er-sin-nen, seid ge - dun-gen und ge - zwun-gen für ein Jahr un - wan-del -
taught that there is naught now But to_ go with them and show that you can do your du - ty_
win-nen und er-sin-nen, seid ge - dun-gen und ge - zwun-gen für ein Jahr un - wan-del -
taught that there is naught now But to_ go with them and show that you can do your du - ty_
win-nen und er-sin-nen, seid ge - dun-gen und ge - zwun-gen für ein Jahr un - wan-del -
taught that there is naught now But to_ go with them and show that you can do your du - ty_
Lady H.
Ach kein Ent-rin-nen ist von hinnen, was er - sinnen zu be-ginnen? ach, verlacht, wird's hinter-
Ah, you are caught now, we'll be taught now That we've sought a sor-ry lot now, We must go with them and
Nancy.
Ach kein Ent-rin-nen ist von hinnen, was er - sinnen zu be-ginnen? ach, verlacht, wird's hinter-
Ah, you are caught now, we'll be taught now That we've sought a sor-ry lot now, We must go with them and
Lionel.
Ach kein Ent-rin-nen ist von hinnen, was er - sinnen zu be-ginnen? seid ge-dungen und ge-
Ah, you are caught now, and you ought now To be taught that there is naught now, But to go with us and
Tristram.
Ach kein Ent-rin-nen ist von hinnen, was er - sinnen zu be-ginnen? ja, verlacht, wird's hinter-
Ah, you are caught now, you'll be taught now That you've sought a sor-ry lot now, you must go with them and
Plunkett.
Ach kein Ent-rin-nen ist von hinnen, was er - sinnen zu be-ginnen? seid ge-dungen und ge-
Ah, you are caught now, and you ought now To be taught that there is naught now, But to go with us and
bar, kein Entrin-nen ist von hinnen zu ge-win-nen und er-sin-nen, seid ge-dungen und er-
well, You are caught now, and you ought now To be taught that there is naught now But to go with them and
bar, kein Entrin-nen ist von hinnen zu ge-win-nen und er-sin-nen, seid ge-dungen und er-
well, You are caught now, and you ought now To be taught that there is naught now But to go with them and
bar, kein Entrin-nen ist von hinnen zu ge-win-nen und er-sin-nen, seid ge-dungen und er-
well, You are caught now, and you ought now To be taught that there is naught now But to go with them and

H.
bracht, sind wir fürwahr auf immer-dar.
show that we their bargain quite re-pel.
N.
bracht, sind wir fürwahr auf immer-dar.
show that we their bargain quite re-pel.
L.
zwungen für ein Jahr un-wandel-bar.
show that you can do your du-ty well.
T.
bracht, sind sie fürwahr auf immer-dar.
show that you can do your du-ty well.
(Lionel and Plunkett lead away the reluctant Lady H. & Nancy.)
P.
zwungen für ein Jahr un-wandel-bar.
show that you can do your du-ty well.
zwungen für ein Jahr un-wandel-bar. Topp! Mädel, 's gilt der Kauf! Topp! nahmt das Hand-geld
show that you can do your du-ty well. Come girls, you gave your word, It can-not be de-
zwungen für ein Jahr un-wandel-bar. Topp! Wer hier stört den Kauf? Topp! kriegt das Handgeld
show that you can do your du-ty well. Come, girls, you gave your word, It cannot be de-
zwungen für ein Jahr un-wandel-bar. Topp! Wer hier stört den Kauf? Topp! kriegt das Handgeld
show that you can do your du-ty well. Come, girls, you gave your word, It can-not be de-
d'rauf! Topp! Mädel, 's gilt der Kauf! Topp! nahmt das Hand-gelt d'rauf!
ferr'd! Come, girls you gave your word, It can-not be de-ferr'd!
d'rauf! Topp! wer hier stört den Kauf? Topp! kriegt das Handgelt d'rauf! Topp! Topp!
ferr'd! Come, girls you gave your word, It can-not be de-ferr'd! come, come,
d'rauf! Topp! wer hier stört den Kauf? Topp! kriegt das Handgelt d'rauf! Topp!
ferr'd! Come, girls you gave your word, It can-not be de-ferr'd! come,

Mäg - de, halt Euch treu, sonst kommt die Reu' gar
Let your deal-ings all be fair and true, Then
Topp! Topp! Topp! Topp! Topp!
come, you gave your word!
Mäg - de, halt Euch treu, sonst kommt die Reu' gar
Let your deal-ings all be fair and true, Then
Topp! Topp! Topp! Topp! Topp!
come, you gave your word!
Mäg - de, halt Euch treu, sonst kommt die Reu' gar
Let your deal-ings all be fair and true, Then
ff
flink her-bei, wenn man thöricht brach, was man versprach, dann kommt die Schmach. Mägde, halt Euch treu, sonst
none shall rue, Prom-ise naught but what is hon-or's law With-out a flaw, Let your dealings all be
flink her-bei, wenn man thöricht brach, was man versprach, dann kommt die Schmach. Mägde, halt Euch treu, sonst
none shall rue, Prom-ise naught but what is hon-or's law With-out a flaw, Let your dealings all be
flink her-bei, wenn man thöricht brach, was man versprach, dann kommt die Schmach. Mägde, halt Euch treu, sonst
none shall rue, Prom-ise naught but what is hon-or's law With-out a flaw, Let your dealings all be
kommt die Reu' gar flink her-bei, wenn man thöricht brach, was man versprach, dann kommt die Schmach, dann
fair and true, Then none shall rue, Promise naught but what is hon-or's law With-out a flaw, nor
kommt die Reu' gar flink her-bei, wenn man thöricht brach, was man versprach, dann kommt die Schmach, dann
fair and true, Then none shall rue, Promise naught but what is hon-or's law With-out a flaw, nor
kommt die Reu' gar flink her-bei, wenn man thöricht brach, was man versprach, dann kommt die Schmach, dann
fair and true, Then none shall rue, Promise naught but what is hon-or's law With-out a flaw, nor

(While Tristram is pushed aside by the angry farmers, Lionel and Plunkett are seen to drive off with the ladies in an open conveyance.)

End of Act I.

Act II.

Interior of the farmhouse; doors at the sides, a centre door leads into the open (where is seen a bell fixed on a pole). At the back R. H. a window, before which stands a bench. In the front L. H. a table and some low settles. In the corner R. H. two spinning-wheels; a lamp is burning on the table.

Nº 7. Entr'acte and Quartettino._ „Nur näher, blöde Mädchen."

Flute, Piccolo, Oboes, Clarinets in A, Bassoons, Horns in A & E, Trumpets in A, Trombones, Ophicleide, Kettledrums in A & E, Triangle, Big Drum and Strings_ afterwards Harp.

Lionel.
L.
H.
Nur nä - her, blö-de Mädchen, wir sind an unserm Ziel.
Plunkett. Come in, ye timid damsels, At last ye are at home.
Lady H.
O
Nancy. A -
P.
N.
Nur nä - her, blö-de Mädchen, wir sind an unserm Ziel. O
Come in, ye timid damsels, At last ye are at home. A -
Cl.
p
Hn. & Cl.
H.
weh! wir armen Mädchen, wir büssen un - ser Spiel! Wir sind in ih - rem
las, we wretched damsels, To grief at last we've come! The place seems dim and
N.
weh! wir armen Mädchen, wir büssen un - ser Spiel! Wir sind in ih - rem
las, we wretched damsels, To grief at last we've come! The place seems dim and
Lionel.
L.
Ihr seid in unserm
The way was long and
Plunkett.
P.
Ihr seid in unserm
The way was long and
Ob.
Fl.
Hau - se — ach! wä - ren wir hin - aus! Wir sind in ih - rem
drea - ry, Ah, soon t'escape were best, The place seems dim and
Hau - se — ach! wä - ren wir hin - aus! Wir sind in ih - rem
drea - ry, Ah, soon t'escape were best, The place seems dim and
Hau - se — jetzt ruht getrost Euch aus, Ihr seid in unserm
wea - ry, Now ye shall take your rest, The way was long and
Hau - se, jetzt ruht getrost Euch aus, Ihr seid in unserm
wea - ry, Now ye shall take your rest, The way was long and

H.
Hau - se, ach! wä-ren wir hin - aus, ach! wä - ren wir hin -
drea - ry, Ah, soon t'escape were best, ah, soon t'escape were
N.
Hau - se, ach! wä-ren wir hin - aus, wä-ren wir hin - aus, wä-ren wir hin -
drea - ry, Ah, soon t'escape were best, soon t'escape were best, soon t'escape were
L.
Hau - se, jetzt ruht ge-trost Euch aus, jetzt ruht ge-trost Euch
wea - ry, Now ye shall take your rest, now ye shall take your
P.
Hau - se, jetzt ruht ge-trost Euch aus, jetzt ruht ge-trost Euch
wea - ry, Now ye shall take your rest, now ye shall take your
Allegro.
aus, wir sind in ihrem Hau - se, ach, wä-ren wir hin - aus!
best, The place seems dim and drea - ry, Ah, soon t'escape were best!
aus, ach, wären wir hinaus, ach, wären wir, ach, wären wir hin - aus!
best, ah, soon t'escape were best, ah, soon t'escape, ah, soon t'escape were best!
aus, jetzt ruht getrost Euch aus, jetzt ruht getrost, jetzt ruht getrost Euch aus.
rest, now ye shall take, now ye shall take your rest, now ye shall take your rest.
aus, jetzt ruht getrost, getrost Euch aus, jetzt ruht getrost Euch aus.
rest, now ye shall take, shall take your rest, now ye shall take your rest.
Ob.
Allegro.
ff Tutti Wind
Lionel.
Früh -
Now
Plunkett.
Früh -
Now
Str. Hns. & Tri'gle

auf, wohlauf! früh-auf, wohlauf! dann schafft die Ar-beit schon! Früh-auf, wohlauf! früh-
haste to rest, now haste to rest, your work be - gins at dawn! Now haste to rest, now
auf, wohlauf! dann schafft die Ar-beit schon! O weh! o weh! o weh! o weh! wer
haste to rest, your work be - gins at dawn! A - las, a-las, what shall we do? The
Lady H.
Nancy.
hilft uns nun da-von? wie kon-nen wir ent-ge - hen den Äng - sten,
jest I sore-ly rue, A - lone and un-pro-tect - ed, With these pre -
die uns droh'n? Dann soll Euch nicht ent-ge - hen der al-ler-beste Lohn, der al-ler-bes-te
sumptuous two. Our thanks are here a - ward-ed For ev'ry service done, for ev'ry service
Lionel.
Plunkett.
die uns droh'n? Der al-ler - beste Lohn, der al-ler-bes-te
sumptuous two. For ev - 'ry service done, for ev'ry service
Str.
NOW YOU'RE HERE WE'LL MAKE IT CLEAR AND HOPE YOU'LL UNDER-STAND? YOU'LL HAVE TO WORK AND
NOT TO SHIRK WHILE YOU ARE ON THE LAND
BUT IF YOU DO YOUR WORK WELL, YOU'LL HAVE YOUR JUST RE-WARD YOU'LL HAVE YOUR JUST RE-

Lady H.
L. H.
Lohn. Wie kön-nen wir ent-ge-hen den Ängsten, die uns droh'n, den Ängsten, die uns
done. Why, for a word un-guard-ed, Such per-il must we run, such per-il must we
Nancy.
P. N.
Lohn. Den Ängsten, die uns droh'n, den Ängsten, die uns
done. Such per-il must we run, such per-il must we
f Wind
p Str.
H.
droh'n, den Äng-sten, die uns droh'n?
run, such per-il must we run?
N.
droh'n, den Äng-sten, die uns droh'n, den Äng-sten, die uns droh'n, ja,
run, such per-il must we run, such per-il must we run? Ah
Lionel.
L.
Frühauf, dann schafft die Ar-beit schon, frühauf, dann schafft die Ar-beit schon, die
Now haste, your work begins at dawn, now haste, your work begins at dawn, be-
Plunkett.
P.
Frühauf, dann schafft die Ar-beit schon, frühauf, dann schafft die Ar-beit schon, die
Now haste, your work begins at dawn, now haste, your work begins at dawn, be-
cresc.
f Tutti
H.
O weh, o weh, o weh, wer hilft uns da-von,
A las, a-las, a-las, what shall we do?
N.
die uns droh'n?
why, ah why?
O weh, o weh, wer hilft uns nun, wer hilft uns
A-las, a-las, what shall we do? a-las, a-
L.
Ar-beit schon!
gins at dawn!
Frühauf, wohlauf, dann schafft die Arbeit schon, dann
Now haste to rest, your work begins at dawn, your
P.
Ar-beit schon!
gins at dawn!
Frühauf, wohlauf, dann schafft die Arbeit schon, dann
Now haste to rest, your work begins at dawn, your
cresc.
p Str
Wind

o weh, o weh, o weh, wer hilft uns da - von, o
a - las, a - las, a - las, ah what shall we do? a -
nun da - von, da - von, wie kön - nen wir entgeh'n, entgeh'n den Ängsten, die uns drohn, o
las, what shall we do, a - las, the jest I sore - ly rue, the jest I sore - ly rue, a
schafft die Arbeit schon, dann soll Euch nicht entgeh'n, entgeh'n der al - ler - bes - te Lohn, früh-
work begins at dawn; our thanks shall here award - ed be for ev - 'ry service done, now
schafft die Arbeit schon, dann soll Euch nicht entgeh'n, entgeh'n der al - ler - bes - te Lohn, früh-
work begins at dawn; our thanks shall here award - ed be for ev - 'ry service done, now
Str.
Wind
weh, o weh, o weh, wer hilft uns da - von, o weh, o weh, o
las, a - las, the jest now sorely I rue, a - las, a - las, a -
weh, o weh, o weh, wer hilft uns nun da - von, wer hilft uns nun da - von, o weh, o
las, a - las, a - las, a - las, what shall we do, a - las, what shall we do, what shall we
auf, wohlauf, dann schafft die Ar - beit schon, dann schafft die Arbeit schon, früh-auf, wohlauf, früh-
haste to rest, your work begins at dawn, your work begins at dawn, now haste, now haste to
auf, wohlauf, dann schafft die Ar - beit schon, dann schafft die Arbeit schon, früh-auf, wohlauf, früh-
haste to rest, your work begins at dawn, your work begins at dawn, now haste, now haste to
Str.
Wind
Str.
Più animato.
weh, wer hilft uns nun da - von, o weh, wer hilft uns nun da -
las, I the jest sorely rue, a - las, the jest I sore - ly
weh! weh, o weh, wer hilft uns nun da -
do? ah, the jest, the jest I sore - ly
auf, auf, früh - auf, dann schafft die Ar - beit
rest, haste to rest, your work be - gins at
auf, auf, früh - auf, dann schafft die Ar - beit
rest, haste to rest, your work be - gins at
Più animato.
f Tutti

H.
von, o weh, wer hilft uns nun da - von, o weh, o
rue, a - las, the jest I sore - ly rue, a - las, what
N.
von, o weh, wer hilft uns nun da - von, o weh, o
rue, a - las, the jest I sore - ly rue, a - las, what
L.
schon, früh - auf, dann schafft die Ar - beit schon, frühauf, wohl-
dawn, now haste, your work be - gins at dawn, now haste, now
P.
Wind
H.
weh, wer hilft, o weh, wer hilft uns nun, o weh, wer hilft uns nun da-
shall we do? a - las, what shall we do? a - las, a - las, what shall we
N.
weh, wer hilft, o weh, wer hilft uns nun, o weh, wer hilft uns nun da-
shall we do? a - las, what shall we do? a - las, a - las, what shall we
L.
auf, dann schafft, dann schafft die Ar - beit schon, frühauf, dann schafft die Ar - beit
haste to rest, your work be-gins at dawn, now haste to rest, now haste to
P.
Tutti
Wind
Tutti
Str. & Wood
H.
von, wer hilft uns nun da - von? o weh!
do? ah, the jest now I sore - ly rue.
N.
von, wer hilft uns nun da - von? o weh!
do? ah, the jest now I sore - ly rue.
L.
schon, dann schafft die Ar - beit schon.
rest, your work be - gins at dawn.
P.
ff Tutti

Nº 8. Recit._„Mädels! dort ist Eure Kammer!“

Nancy. Plunkett. Nancy (hesitating). Plunkett.
P.
N.
Du? Was ich nur sa-ge?- Weisst Du's selbst nicht? Ju - li - a! Ju-li-a?
you? (What shall I tell him?) Don't you know it? Ju - li - a! Ju-li-a?
p str.
P.
welch stol-zer Na-me! Ju-li-a! lass Dich herab, Ju - li - a, Du gro-sse
Too grand to please me! Ju-li-a! pray condescend, Ju - li - a, my dame of
(gives them to her) Nancy (throwing them down). Plunkett (in a rage). Lionel.
P.
N.
P.
L.
Da - me, nimm mir Hut und Mantel ab. Thut Ihr's selbst! Ha, al-le Tau - send! Nicht so
fash - ion, put my cloak and hat a - way. Do't your-self. What's this im-pert -'nence! Pray be
f
L.
hef-tig, nicht so brausend! sprich doch sanft und mild wie ich — Martha,
gen-tle and con-sid-'rate, see, I'll put them quite at ease— Martha,
p
(Giving her his hat; she looks at him haughtily, he steps back abashed.)
L.
nimm! ich bit - te Dich.
take it, if you please.
f
Tutti

Quartet.– „Was soll ich dazu sagen?“

H.
wun-dert steh'n, hier gilt es nicht ver-za-gen, sonst ist's um uns, um uns ge-
what to say. No pleasant sit-u-a-tion, Would that we both were far a-
L.
von ei-ner Magd geseh'n, was soll ich da-zu sa-gen? wie ist mir denn ge-
To say a mas-ter nay, I'm fill'd with conster-na-tion, I know not what to
P.
von ei-ner Magd geseh'n, was soll ich da-zu sa-gen? wie ist mir denn ge-
To say a mas-ter nay, I'm fill'd with conster-na-tion, I know not what to
Lady H.
pp
Er weiss nicht, was zu sa-gen, und bleibt, und bleibt ver-wundert steh'n;
He eyes me with vex-a-tion, He knows not what, not what to say.
N.
scheh'n! Er weiss nicht, was zu sa-gen, und bleibt verwundert
way! He's lost in conster-na-tion, He knows not what to
L.
scheh'n? was soll ich da-zu sa-gen? wie ist mir denn ge-
say, I'm fill'd with conster-na-tion, I know not what to
P.
scheh'n? was soll ich da-zu sa-gen? wie ist mir denn ge-
say, I'm fill'd with conster-na-tion, I know not what to
pp
H.
macht ihn mein Anblick za-gen? erkennt, erkennt er sein Vergeh'n? Ja! er kann nichts sagen,
Out of this sit-u-a-tion, Were I a hundred miles a-way! lost in conster-nation,
N.
steh'n, hier gilt es nicht ver-zagen, sonst ist's um uns gescheh'n! Ja! er kann nichts sagen,
say, No pleasant sit-u-a-tion, Would we were far a-way! lost in conster-nation,
L.
scheh'n? Nie hat man solch Betra-gen ge-seh'n! Ha! was soll ich sagen?
say, no, no, I do not know what to say, ne'er has't been the fashion
P.
scheh'n? Nie hat man solch Betra-gen ge-seh'n! Ha! was soll ich sagen?
say, no, no, I do not know what to say, ne'er has't been the fashion

H.
N.
L.
P.
und bleibt verwundert steh'n; macht ihn mein Anblick za - gen? er - kennt er sein Ver -
He knows not what to say, Out of this sit - u - a - tion, Would I were far a -
und bleibt verwundert steh'n; hier gilt es, nicht ver-za - gen, sonst ist's um uns ge -
He knows not what to say, No plea-sant sit - u - a - tion, Would we were far a -
wie ist mir denn ge-scheh'n? Nie hat man solch Be-tra - gen von ei ner Magd ge -
To say a mas-ter nay, Ne'er has it been the fash - ion To say a mas - ter
Wind
Str.
geh'n? Er bleibt ver - wun - dert steh'n, macht ihn, macht ihn mein Anblick
way, He knows not what to say, Ah me, he eyes me with vex -
scheh'n, ja, er bleibt ver - wundert steh'n, hier gilt es, nicht ver - za - gen, sonst
way, Would that we were far a - way, He's lost in con - ster - na - tion, He
seh'n, nie hat man solch Be - tra - gen von ei - ner Magd geseh'n,
nay, Ne'er has it been the fash - ion To say a mas - ter nay,
cresc.
f
pp
za - gen? erkennt, erkennt, er sein Ver-geh'n, er-kennt er sein Ver-geh'n? Ja, er
a - tion, He knows not what, he knows not what, he knows not what to say, what to
ist's, sonst ist's um uns gescheh'n, sonst ist's um uns, ja, um uns gescheh'n, ja, er
knows, he knows not what to say, he knows not what, knows not what to say, what to
nein, nie hat man solch Be-tra-gen von ei - ner Magd ge-seh'n, wie ist
No, ne'er has it been the fash-ion To say a mas-ter nay, I know
Str.

dol.
H.
bleibt ver - wun - dert steh'n, er weiss nicht, was zu sa - gen, und bleibt ver -
say, not what to say, Out of this sit - u - a - tion, Would that I
N.
bleibt ver - wun - dert steh'n, er weiss nicht, was zu sa - gen, und bleibt ver -
say, not what to say, No pleasant sit - u - a - tion Would that we
L.
mir denn ge - scheh'n, ge - scheh'n? was soll ich da - zu sa - gen? wie ist mir
not what to say - no, no, I'm fill'd with conster - na - tion, I know not
P.
mir denn ge - scheh'n, ge - scheh'n?
not what to say - no, no,
Cl.
dolce
Wind
wun - dert steh'n, ver - wundert steh'n, macht ihn mein Anblick
were a hun - dred miles a - way, He eyes me with vex -
cresc.
wundert steh'n, ver wun - dert steh'n, ver - wundert steh'n, hier gilt es, nicht ver -
were a hundred miles a hun - dred miles a - way, No plea - sant sit - u -
denn, wie ist mir denn gescheh'n? nie hat man solch Be - tra - gen von ei - ner
what, I know not what to say, Ne'er has it been the fash - ion Thus, thus to
Tutti
zagen, erkennt, er - kennt er sein Ver - geh'n?
a - tion, I'd be a hun - dred miles a - way.
f
zagen, sonst ist's sonst ist's um uns gescheh'n!
a - tion, I'd be a hun - dred miles a - way.
Magd, von ei - ner Magd ge - seh'n!
say, to say a mas - ter nay.
(The farmers put away their cloaks themselves.)
ff
p

Allegro moderato.
Lady H.
Plunkett.
Spinnen,
To our
Na, jetzt hurtig, ohne Zaudern, holt das Spinnrad.
Now then, girls, be up and doing; to your spinning!
Allegro moderato.
Str.
Wind
Nancy.
Lionel
THAT YOU'LL HAVE TO
Spinnen? Spinnen wir? Nun ja freilich!
spinning? We to spin? What a question!
Die-net Ihr in der Wirthschaft nur zum
Do you think you'll do nothing but the
Str.
Lady H.
Nancy.
Ha, ha, ha, ha, ha, ha! Spinnen! Ha, ha, ha, ha, ha, ha! Spinnen! (mimicking)
Ha, ha, ha, ha, ha, ha! spinning! Ha, ha, ha, ha, ha, ha! spinning!
Plaudern?
chatting?
Ha, ha,
Ha, ha,
Wood
Str. & Wind
Hns.
ha, ha, ha, ha! Spinnen! Ei zum Blitz! ei zum Blitz! seid Ihr denn zu gar nichts
ha, ha, ha, ha! spinning! Can it be, this is it, That you are for no-thing

Nancy.
N.
P.
Ja, nur
Do not
(angrily)
nütz, und wollt doch den Lohn ge - win-nen? Her die Räder!
fit? Why d'ye think that we en - gag'd you? Fetch the spindles!
Str.
Lady H.
Lionel.
H.
L.
Ja, nur stil - le! Sei doch sanft, du schreckst sie ja!
Do not scold us! Oh, speak gen-tly, broth - er, pray!
Nancy.
(They run and fetch the spindles.)
Plunkett.
stil-le, ja, nur stil - le!
scold us, do not scold us!
Schweig'! Jetzt spinnt! Es ist mein
Stuff! Now spin, girls, I com-
Lady H.
Nancy.
Lionel.
Kann's nicht!
I can't!
Kann's nicht!
I can't!
Wie?
What!
(posed)
Wil-le!
mand you!
Was? Ah!
What! Ah!
pp Wood
Str.
Lady H. (terrified; they sit down at the wheels).
Ja, doch!
Gracious!
(rudely)
Nancy (terrified).
Setzt Euch!
Sit down!
Ja, doch!
Gracious!
fp
ff
fp

Plunkett.
P.
N.
Dreht das Rädchen, schnurr, schnurr, schnurr, schnurr! Will sich nicht
Turn the wheel round, brr, brr, brr, brr! It will not
Nancy.
fp
f
p
Lady H.
H.
L.
Will sich nicht dreh'n.
It will not turn.
Lionel.
Zieht vom Flachs ein dün-nes
Twist the slen-der thread of
dreh'n.
turn.
Plunkett.
Schnurr, schnurr, schnurr, schnurr, schnurr, schnurr, schnurr, schnurr, schnurr, schnurr,
Brr, brr, brr, brr, brr, brr, brr, brr, brr, brr,
f
p
Lady H.
Es will nicht geh'n, es will nicht ge-hen!
It will not turn, I can-not learn it!
Nancy.
Es will nicht geh'n, es will nicht ge-hen!
It will not turn, I can-not learn it!
Fäd-chen, nur recht fein, nur recht fein!
flax, nor hold it tight, nor too lax!
Drehet!
Turn it!
schnurr, schnurr, schnurr, schnurr, schnurr! schnurr!
brr, brr, brr, brr, brr, brr!
Drehet!
Turn it!
f
p

H.
N.
L.
P.
'S dreht nicht! Es geht nicht! Kann nicht! Nein! Versteh's nicht!
Use - less! I can-not! Use - less! Can't! I can-not,
'S dreht nicht! Es geht nicht! Kann nicht! Nein! Ver-
Use - less! I can-not! Use - less! Can't!
Zieht! Tre-tet! Geht's nicht? Ihr ver-
Draw! Turn it! Fast - er! How, you
Zieht! Tre-tet! Geht's nicht? So, so!
Draw! Turn it! Fast - er! Like this!
cresc. poco a poco
Versteh's nicht! Macht's uns vor, macht's uns vor.
'Tis use-less! show me how, show me how.
steh's nicht! Versteh's nicht! Macht's uns vor, macht's uns vor.
can-not! 'Tis use-less! show me how, show me how.
steht's nicht? Ihr ver-steht's nicht?
can-not? How, you can-not?
So, so! So
Like this! I'll
Tutti
(seats himself at the wheel)
Allegretto non troppo.
muss es sein! Immer munter dreht das
show you how! This way set the wheel a -
Str. con sordini
Hns. sustain
'Cello & Bass pizz.

Lady H.
Ah! zu lus-tig, ah,
How de-lightful, ah,
Nancy.
Nein, zu lus-tig, wie am Rädchen Her-ku-
How the bu-sy task he's ply-ing, Her-cu-
Lionel.
Immer munter dreht das Rädchen, auf und
Come, you will not lose by try-ing, I can
Plunkett.
Rädchen, immer munter dreht das Rädchen, immer munter dreht das Rädchen, auf und
fly-ing, set it whirring, set it fly-ing, set it whirring, set it fly-ing, Work the
ah!
ah!
les bewegt das Brett! Wie er zierlich zieht das Fädchen, dass im Schnurren fein sich's
les is at the wheel! How the gold-en thread is fly-ing Thro' his fingers with a
'runter lasst das Brett, fein, ihr Mädchen, zieht das Fädchen, dass das Rädchen schnurrend
see you have good will, While the gold-en thread you're plying, Sing a mer-ry measure
'runter lasst das Brett, fein, ihr Mädchen, zieht das Fädchen, dass das Rädchen schnurrend
treadle with a will, While an e-ven thread you're plying, Never let your wheel be
cresc. poco a poco
Nein, zu lustig, wie am Rädchen, wie er
'Tis de-lightful, how the golden thread is
cresc. poco a poco
dreht. Nein zu lus-tig, wie am Rädchen Her-ku-les be-wegt das Brett, wie er
will! How the bu-sy task he's ply-ing, Her-cu-les is at the wheel, How the
cresc. poco a poco
dreht. Im-mer munter dreht das Rädchen, auf und 'runter lasst das Brett, fein, ihr
still. Come, you will not loose by try-ing, I can see you have good will, While the
cresc. poco a poco
dreht. Schnurr, schnurr, schnurr, schnurr, schnurr, schnurr, schnurr, schnurr, schnurr,
still. Brr, brr, brr, brr, brr, brr, brr, brr, brr,
cresc. poco a poco

H.
zierlich zieht das Fädchen, ha, ha, ha, ha, ha, ha,
fly-ing thro' his fingers, ha, ha, ha, ha, ha, ha,
N.
zierlich zieht das Fädchen, ha, ha, ha, ha, ha, dass das
golden thread is flying, ha, ha, ha, ha, ha, Thro' his
L.
Mädchen, zieht das Fädchen, dass zum Schnurren fein sich's dreht, ja, dass zum
golden thread you're plying, Sing a mer - ry mea - sure still, yes, sing a
P.
schnurr, schnurr, schnurr, schnurr, schnurr, schnurr, schnurr, schnurr, schnurr, schnurr, schnurr, schnurr, schnurr,
brr, brr, brr, brr, brr, brr, brr, brr, brr, brr, brr, brr, brr,
H.
ha, ha, ha, ha, ha, ha! Ha! zu
ha, ha, ha, ha, ha, ha! How de-
N.
Räd - chen schnur-rend dreht, ha, ha, ha, ha! Nein, zu
fin - gers with a will, ha, ha, ha, ha! How the
L.
Schnurren fein sich's dreht, ha, ha, ha, ha! Immer
mer - ry mea - sure still, ha, ha, ha, ha! Come, you
P.
schnurr, schnurr, schnurr, schnurr, schnurr, schnurr, schnurr, schnurr, schnurr. Immer
brr, brr, brr, brr, brr, brr, brr, brr, brr. This way
f Tutti
ff p str.
H.
lustig, ah, ah!
lightful, ah, ah!
N.
lustig, wie am Rädchen Herku - les bewegt das Brett, wie er zierlich zieht das
bu - sy task he's plying, Her-cu - les is at the wheel, How the golden thread is
L.
munter dreht das Rädchen, auf und 'runter lasst das Brett, fein, ihr Mädchen, zieht das
will not lose by trying, I can see you have good will, While the golden thread you're
P.
munter dreht das Rädchen, auf und 'runter lasst das Brett, fein, ihr Mädchen, zieht das
set the wheel a - flying, Work the treadle with good will, While the golden thread you're

cresc. poco a poco
H.
Nein, zu lus-tig!
How de-lightful!
N.
cresc.
Fädchen, dass im Schnurren fein sich's dreht! Nein, zu lustig, wie am Rädchen Her-ku-
flying Thro' his fin-gers with a will! How the bu-sy task he's plying, Her-cu-
L.
cresc.
Fädchen, dass das Rädchen schnurrend dreht! Im-mer munter dreht das Rädchen, auf und
plying Sing a mer-ry measure still! Come, you will not lose by trying, I can
P.
cresc.
Fädchen, dass das Rädchen schnurrend dreht! Schnurr schnurr, schnurr, schnurr, schnurr,
plying, Let your wheel be nev-er still! Brr, brr, brr, brr, brr,
cresc. poco a poco
cresc.
wie am Rädchen er so zierlich zieht das Fädchen, ha, ha, ha,
how the gold-en thread is flying thro' his fingers, ha, ha, ha,
cresc.
les bewegt das Brett, wie er zierlich zieht das Fädchen, dass im Schnur-ren fein sich's
les is at the wheel, How the golden thread is flying Thro' his fin-gers with a
cresc.
'run-ter lasst das Brett, fein, ihr Mädchen, zieht das Fädchen, dass das Rädchen schnurrend
see you have good will, While the golden thread you're ply-ing, Sing a mer-ry measure
cresc.
f
schnurr, schnurr, schnurr! Fein, ihr Mädchen, zieht das Fädchen! Schnurr, schnurr, schnurr!
brr, brr, brr! While an e-ven thread you're plying, brr, brr, brr!
cresc.
f p
ha! Ah,
ha! Ah,
f p
dreht. Nein, zu lustig, wie am Rädchen Her-ku-les bewegt das Brett, wie ihr
will! How the bu-sy task he's plying, Her-cu-les is at the wheel, How the
f p
dreht. Immer munter dreht das Rädchen, auf und 'run-ter lasst das Brett, fein, ihr
still, Come, you will not lose by try-ing, I can see you have good will, While the
p
Immer munter dreht das Rädchen, auf und 'run-ter lasst das Brett, fein, ihr
This way set the wheel a-flying, Work the treadle with a will, While an
ff Tutti
p Str.
p

H.
N.
zierlich zieht das Fädchen, dass im Schnurren fein sich's dreht, ja, fein sich's dreht,
golden thread is flying Thro' his fingers with a will, yes, with a will,
L.
Mädchen, zieht das Fädchen, dass das Rädchen schnurrend dreht, ja, schnurrend dreht,
golden thread you're ply-ing Sing a mer-ry measure still, a measure still,
P.
Mädchen, zieht das Fädchen, dass das Rädchen schnurrend dreht, ja, schnurrend dreht,
e-ven thread you're plying Let your wheel be nev-er still, no, nev-er still,
dass es— fein sich dreht.
fly-ing— with a will.
Ja doch, ja!
Thank you, yes!
ja, fein sich's dreht.
yes, with a will.
Ja doch, ja!
Thank you, yes!
ja, schnurrend dreht.
yes, sing it still.
Seht Ihr, seht Ihr!
Now you've learnt it?
ja, schnurrend dreht.
no, nev-er still.
Seht Ihr, seht Ihr!
Now you've learnt it?
ff Tutti
Ja doch, ja!
Here's a pass!
Ja doch, ja!
Here's a pass!
Und versteht Ihr?
Work a-way then!
Seht Ihr, seht Ihr und versteht Ihr, und ver-
If you've learnt it, work a-way then, work a-
Und versteht Ihr?
Work a-way then!
Seht Ihr, seht Ihr und versteht Ihr, und ver-
If you've learnt it, work a-way then, work a-

(All laugh)
H.
N.
L.
P.
Ja doch, ja! Ha, ha, ha, ha, ha, ha, ha, ha, ha, ha, ha, ha, ha, ha, ha,
Here's a pass! Ha, ha, ha, ha, ha, ha, ha, ha, ha, ha, ha, ha, ha, ha, ha,
steht Ihr, und ver - steht Ihr? Ha, ha, ha, ha, ha, ha, ha,
way if you have learnt it. Ha, ha, ha, ha, ha, ha, ha,
ha, ha, ha, ha, ha, ha, ha, ha, ha, ha, ha, ha, ha, ha, ha, ha, ha! Ah! zu lus-tig ah!
ha, ha, ha, ha, ha, ha, ha, ha, ha, ha, ha, ha, ha, ha, ha, ha, ha! How de-lightful, ah!
Nein, zu lus-tig, wie am Rädchen Her-ku - les bewegt das Brett, wie er zierlich zieht das Fädchen, dass im
How the bu sy task he's plying, Her-cu - les is at the wheel! Look, I too can set it flying, Scold me
Immer mun-ter dreht das Rädchen, auf und 'runter lasst das Brett, fein, ihr Mädchen, zieht das Fädchen, dass das
Soon you see you've learnt by try-ing, I was sure you have good will, While the golden thread you're ply-ing, Sing a
This way set the wheel a - flying, Work the treadle with a will, While an e-ven thread you're plying, Let your
p Hns.
p Str.

cresc. poco a poco
H.
Nein, zu lustig, wie am
How de-lightful! I will
N.
Schnurren fein sich's dreht! Nein, zu lustig, wie am Rädchen Her-ku-les bewegt das
if I do it ill! How the bu-sy task he's ply-ing, Her-cu-les is at the
L.
Rädchen schnurrend dreht! Im-mer munter dreht das Rädchen, auf und 'run-ter lasst das
mer-ry measure still! Soon, you see, you've learnt by try-ing, I was sure you had good
P.
Rädchen schnurrend dreht! Schnurr, schnurr, schnurr, schnurr, schnurr, schnurr, schnurr,
wheel be nev-er still! Brr, brr, brr, brr, brr, brr, brr,
cresc. poco a poco
Rädchen er so zierlich zieht das Fädchen, ha, ha, ha, ha! Ah!
try and set it flying Thro' my fingers, ha, ha, ha, ha! Ah!
Brett, wie er zierlich zieht das Fädchen, dass im Schnurren fein sich's dreht. Nein, zu
wheel, Look, I too can set it fly-ing, Scold me soon if I do it ill! How the
Brett, fein, ihr Mädchen, zieht das Fädchen, dass das Rädchen schnurrend dreht. Immer
will, While the golden thread you're ply-ing, Sing a mer-ry measure still. Soon you
schnurr, fein, ihr Mädchen, zieht das Fädchen, schnurr, schnurr, schnurr. Immer
brr, While an e-ven thread you're plying, brr, brr, brr. This way
ff Tutti
lus-tig, wie am Rädchen Her-ku-les bewegt das Brett, wie er zierlich zieht das
bu-sy task he's plying, Her-cu-les is at the wheel, Look, I too can set it
munter dreht das Rädchen, auf und 'runter lasst das Brett, fein, ihr Mädchen, zieht das
see you've learnt by try-ing, I was sure you had good will, While the golden thread is
munter dreht das Rädchen, auf und 'runter lasst das Brett, fein, ihr Mädchen, zieht das
set the wheel a-fly-ing, Work the treadle with a will, While an e-ven thread you're
p Str.

Ossia
molto ritenuto
molto animato
Nein, zu
Ah the
colla voce
Fädchen, dass im Schnurren fein sich's dreht, ja, dass sich's dreht, nein, zu
fly-ing, Scold me if I do it ill, if I do't ill, ah the
colla voce
Fädchen, dass das Rädchen schnurrend dreht, ja, dass sich's dreht, im-mer
fly-ing, Sing a mer-ry mea-sure still, a mea - sure still, see how
colla voce
Fädchen, dass das Rädchen schnurrend dreht, ja, dass sich's dreht, im-mer
ply-ing, Mind your wheel is nev-er still, is nev - er still, see how
molto animato
colla voce
Tutti
lus-tig, wie am Rädchen der Päch-ter tritt das Brett, wie er zierlich zieht das Fädchen, dass
bu-sy task I'm ply-ing, I too can guide the wheel, how the golden thread does fly thro' my
lus-tig, wie am Rädchen der Päch-ter tritt das Brett, wie er zierlich zieht das Fädchen, dass
bu-sy task I'm ply-ing, I too can guide the wheel, how the golden thread does fly thro' my
mun-ter dreht das Rädchen, und zier-lich zieht das Fädchen, ja, zierlich zieht das Fädchen, dass
soon you've learnt by try-ing, I knew you had good will, while the golden thread you ply, sing a
mun-ter dreht das Rädchen, und zier-lich zieht das Fädchen, ja, zierlich zieht das Fädchen, dass
soon you've learnt by try-ing, I knew you had good will, while an e-ven thread you ply, let your

H.
schnurrend es sich dreht, wie er zierlich zieht das Fädchen, dass im Schnurren fein sich's dreht, dass im
fin-gers with a will, how the golden thread is fly-ing thro' my fingers with a will, how the
N.
schnurrend es sich dreht, wie er zierlich zieht das Fädchen, dass im Schnurren fein sich's dreht, dass im
fin-gers with a will, how the golden thread is fly-ing thro' my fingers with a will, how the
L.
schnurrend es sich dreht, fein, ihr Mädchen, zieht das Fädchen, dass das Rädchen schnurrend dreht, dass das
mer-ry measure still, while the golden thread you're plying, sing a mer-ry mea-sure still, while the
P.
schnurrend es sich dreht, fein, ihr Mädchen, zieht das Fädchen, dass das Rädchen schnurrend dreht, dass das
wheel be nev-er still, while an e-ven thread you're plying, let your wheel be nev-er still, while an
H.
Schnurren fein sich's dreht, sich's dreht.
golden thread doth fly, doth fly.
N.
Schnurren fein sich's dreht, sich's dreht.
golden thread doth fly, doth fly.
L.
Rädchen, dass das Räd - chen dreht.
golden thread you ply, you ply.
(Nancy upsets one of the spinning-wheels; he threatens her; she runs away, he following.)
P.
Rädchen, dass das Räd - chen dreht.
e-ven thread you ply, you ply.
ff

Nº 9. Duet.—„Blickt sein Auge doch so ehrlich."

H.
L.
Lionel.
lein! Mein' ich's doch so treu und ehr-lich, lau-ter ist mein Herz und rein:
lone! Is't with fear, or is't with an-ger, That her mer - ry mood hath flown?
Fl. & Ob.
Hns. & Bssn.
Str.
Hns.
L.
den-noch klopft es un - auf - hör-lich, bin ich mit ihr, mit ihr al - lein!
Ah, my heart, my heart's in dan - ger Since I have been with her a - lone!
Vl. arco
dolce legato
L.
Nun! Ich will auch nimmer schel - ten, will nicht streng und herrisch
Come, I promise ne'er to chide you, I'll con-sult your gen-tle
L.
H.
Lady H. (looking round in all directions).
sein. Ja, Dein Wille soll mir gel - ten. Ach, sie lässt mich hier al-lein, ach, sie
will; None shall govern here beside you. Ah, to leave me here was ill, ah, to
Ob. & Cl.
H.
L.
Lionel.
lässt mich hier al - lein! Mar - tha! Lass mich Dir's ge-ste - hen,
leave me here was ill! Mar - tha, ah, let me con-fess it,
Vl.
legato
p Str.

L.
seit dem er-sten Au-gen-blick, dass ich, Hol - de, Dich ge - se - hen -
that my heart for thee doth burn, If thy sweet - ness deign to bless it -
Lady H.
H.
Und sie kommt auch nicht zurück, und sie kommt auch nicht zu - rück! Er wird
Ah, why doth she not re-turn, ah, why doth she not re - turn! Not so
Lionel.
L.
poco più mosso
Mar - tha! Mar-tha!
Mar - tha! Mar-tha!
Cl. & Bssn.
Ob. & Cl.
p Str.
H.
dreister. Ja! Ihr seid zu gut als Meister - ich zu
fast, sir. You're too le - nient for a mas-ter, and to
L.
Brav und red - lich ist mein Sinn.
Ah, thy looks my hopes dis - perse.
H.
schlecht zur Diene - rin. Nur müssig stehen, gaffen,
serve I'm too per-verse. I'm on-ly good to laugh and
L.
Du! zu schlecht? Du! zu schlecht?
You, per-verse? You, per - verse?
Cl.
Ob.
Bssn.
'Cello & Bass

H.
sin-gen, mag ich gern, lasst die träge Magd d'rum ge-hen, lasst die trä - ge Magd d'rum
while the time in play, send the i-dle maid a - way; she'll nev-er give you sa - tis -
Str.
(going)
H.
ge - hen!
fac - tion!
L.
Nein! Ich trüg's nicht, wärst Du fern, wärst Du fern!
Ah, 'tis too late, with-out you life's a blank!
cresc.
Tromb.&Hns. sust.
H.
Herr!
Nay!
L.
Nein! Nicht soll Dich Arbeit quä - len; sin - gen sollst Du,
Ah! No work shall vex or tire you, play and sing the
f Tutti
p Str.
Wind
Str. pizz.
L.
fröhlich sein, und zum Werk soll uns be - see - len Dein Gesang, so fromm und rein,
live-long day, As the hu - mor shall in-spire you, I'll delight near you to stay,

L.
Dein Gesang so fromm und rein.
I'll de-light near you to stay.
Sing' ein Liedchen.
Sing a dit-ty!
Fl.
Str. arco
Hns. & Bssn.
Lady H.
H.
Bin zu blö-de.
Nay, ex-cuse me.
ad lib.
So ein Volks-lied, recht für's Herz,
Sing a lay of days gone by,
so ein Volkslied, recht für's
sing a song that's from the
colla voce
Animato
Kann's nicht
Not now! (Seizes some flowers she wears.)
So lasst den Scherz!
Nay, you're too bold!
Herz. Deinen Strauss, Du Sprö-de! für ein Lied!
heart. I will keep this flow'r till you have sung!
Nein! Ich
I in-
Str. & Wind
Ihr wollt?
In-sist?
Nun ge-hor-chen ist ja Sit-te!
Well, it seems I must o-bey you!
will's! Ich bit-te!
sist! I pray you!
Hns. & Bssn.

Ballad. – „Letzte Rose, wie magst du.“

H.
trau - rig im Gar - ten al - lein? Sollst im Tod mit den
lone one, to pine on the stem; Since the love - ly are
H.
Schwe-stern, mit den Schwestern ver-ei-nigt sein. D'rum pflück' ich, o
sleep - ing, go, sleep thou with them. Thus kind - ly I
ad lib.
a tempo
H.
Ro - se, vom Stam - me, vom Stamme dich ab, sollst ruh'n mir am
scat - ter thy leaves o'er the bed, Where thy mates of the
Wind sust.
H.
Her - zen und mit mir, ja, mit mir im Grab, sollst
gar - den lie scent - - - less and dead, thy
Lionel:
L.
Sollst
thy
cresc.

H.
ruh'n mir am Her-zen und mit mir, ja, mit mir im Grab.
mates of the gar-den lie scent - less and dead.
L.
ruh'n mir am Her-zen und mit mir, ja, mit mir im Grab.
mates of the gar-den lie scent - less and dead.
f Tutti
p dim.
ff
Più animato.
Lionel.
Mar - tha!
Mar - tha!
fp Str. poco marc. Brass
Lady H.
Herr!
Sir!
Lionel.
Lass mich Dir sa-gen, was mit Zau - bers All - ge - walt vor dem Aug' ich se - he ta - gen, dass es
Oh let me tell thee That a pow'r well-nigh di - vine, To con - fess it doth com-pel me Ah, my

L.
bis zum Her - zen strahlt! Mar - tha!
heart no more is mine! Mar - tha!
Lady H.
H.
Lasst mich! Lasst mich!
Leave me! Leave me!
Seit der Stun - de, dass ich Dich sah, dass ich Dich sah_
Since the mo-ment I saw thee first, Oh hear me now_
Ob. & Cl.
Str.
Lasst mich! Fort! Fort!
Leave me! Nay! Nay!
Mar-tha! Mar-tha! O bleib'! O bleib', ach!
Mar-tha! Mar-tha! Oh stay! Oh stay! Ah,
Tutti
cresc.
f
Adagio
Mar - tha,_ nimm zum frommen Bun - de_ mei - ne Hand, mei - ne
Mar - tha,_ from my heart I ask_ thee_ to ac-cept me your
pp
Harp
Hns. & Bssn. sust.

animato
Lady H. (aside).
H.
L.
Grosse Götter! Grosse Götter!
Gracious Heaven! Gracious Heaven!
Hand, o sei, o sei mein Weib! Dir zu Füssen, Dir zu
willing slave! Oh, be my wife! I implore thee I a-
animato
ad lib.
(aside)
(to him)
Fassung! Fassung! Wie? Ihr knieet ja, Herr! Ach, da werd'ich lachen
Heaven! Courage! What? up-on your knees, sir? ah, I can't refrain from
Füssen!
dore thee!
str. colla voce
Animato
Lionel
müssen ach, ver-zeiht! ha, ha, ha, ha! Ich will Dich zu mir er-
laughing, pray for-give ha, ha, ha, ha! I will raise thee to my
str. trem.
fz
Lady H.
he-ben, will ver-ges-sen mei-nen Stand. Mich er-he-ben? Das ist's
sta-tion, pride of rank I here dis-own. You will raise me? I must
p
fz
p

e-ben, was ich gar so lus-tig fand!
laugh in-deed, too droll the scene has grown!
colla voce
Tutti
Andantino
Lionel.
Sie lacht zu meinen Lei-den, ver-höhnt mein treues Herz!
She laughs at my de-jec-tion, She mocks my sorr'wing heart!
legato
Hns. & Bssn.
Str. sust.
ihr Blick scheint sich zu wei-den an mei-nen hei-ssen Schmerz; mein Loos mit
I can-not brook re-jec-tion, 'Twere death from her to part; With her thro'
poco animato
Str. poco animato
mir zu thei-len, verschmäht ihr spröder Sinn! Nichts kann die Wunde
life u-nit-ed, What tongue my bliss could tell! But ah! my hopes are
rit.
cresc.
colla voce
Lady H.
Poco più mosso.
Wie jammert mich sein Lei-den, ach, mich quält des
Too late comes my re-flec-tion, I must wound the
hei-len, fahr' hin, mein Glück fahr' hin!
blighted, Fare-well to joy, fare-well!
Str. & Wind

H.
L.
Lionel
Armen Schmerz_ gar Manche dürft' mich nei - den um sein ge-treu-es Herz! Sein
gentle heart That offers me pro - tec - tion, He'll deep-ly feel the smart! With
Ob.
Loos mit mir zu thei - len, erscheint ihm Hochgewinn, ach, könnt' ich ihm ent-
me thro' life u - nit - ed, His pray'r I must re-pel, His ten-der love is
Mein Loos mit mir zu thei - len, verschmäht ihr spröder Sinn, Nichts kann die Wunde
With her thro' life u - nit - ed, What tongue my bliss could tell! But ah, my hopes are
ei - len, sonst ist sein Glück da - hin, da - hin!
blighted, Would I might say fare-well, fare-well!
hei - len, fahr' hin, mein Glück, fahr' hin, fahr' hin! Fahr'
blighted, Farewell to joy, fare-well, fare-well! Fare -
ff Tutti
Ja, sonst ist sein Glück da - hin, sonst ist sein
Would that I might say fare - well, that I might
hin, mein Gluck, fahr' hin, fahr' hin,
well to joy, fare - well! fare - well,
cresc.

rit.
Glück da-hin, sonst ist sein Glück, sonst ist sein Glück da-
say fare-well, ah, would that I, that I might say fare-
fahr' hin, mein Glück, fahr' hin, fahr' hin, mein Glück, fahr'
fare-well, my joy, fare-well, fare-well, my joy, fare-
f
ff a tempo
hin! Sein Loos mit mir zu theilen, ach, erscheint ihm Hochgewinn, ach, könnt' ich ihm ent-
well! With me thro' life u-nit-ed, Ah! that hope I must re-pel, His ten-der love is
hin! Mein Loos mit mir zu theilen, ach, verschmäht ihr spröder Sinn. Nichts kann die Wunde
well! Thro' life with her u-nit-ed, Ah! what tongue my bliss could tell, But ah, my hopes are
ei-len, sonst ist sein Glück da-hin, sonst ist sein Glück, sein Glück da-hin!
blighted, Ah, would that I might say, ah, would that I might say farewell!
hei-len, fahr' hin, mein Glück, fahr' hin, fahr' hin, mein Glück, mein Glück, fahr' hin!
blighted, Farewell, my joy, farewell, farewell, my joy, my joy, farewell!
colla voce
più animato
ff Tutti

Nº 10. Finale II. — „Warte nur, das sollst Du büssen!“

Enter Plunkett, leading in Nancy by the arm.

Nancy.
P.
N.
kräf - tig. Bin dem Mä - del wirk - lich gut. Mar-tha!
fu - ry, Storm a - way, 'twill do me good. Mar-tha!
f Tutti
Plunkett.
P.
Na! was fehlt Euch bei - den? steht ja so ver-ha-gelt dort;
Well, what is the mat-ter? You're both looking scant of cheer;
p Hns. & Bssn.
P.
mag das Müssig - geh'n nicht lei - den! Marsch mit Euch! Zur Ru-he
I - dle ways I can - not bear with, Come, be brisk, a - way to
Wind
'Cello & Bass
Andante. Notturno.
Lady H.
H.
Mit-ter - nacht, Mit-ter - nacht!
Twelve o' - clock, twelve o' - clock!
Nancy.
N.
Mit-ter - nacht, Mit-ter - nacht!
Twelve o' - clock, twelve o' - clock!
Lionel.
L.
(to Lady H.)
Mitternacht, Mit-ter - nacht! Schlafe
Twelve o'clock, twelve o' - clock! All good
Plunkett.
P.
fort!
bed!
Mit-ter - nacht!
Twelve o' - clock!
Andante.
Vl. con sord.
pp
(clock strikes midnight)
pp
K. dr.

POSE AND HAPPY SLUMBER NOW BE YOURS TILL MORNING LIGHT AH! MAY YOU
L.
wohl! und mag Dich reu - en, was Dein ar-ger Hohn voll-bracht! Ja! O, lass
an - gels watch a - bove thee, And thy scorning put to flight, Ah, tho' no
'Cello & Bass sust.
pp
Harp
HEART BY THEN TO-WARD ME HAVE RE-LENTED SO GOOD NIGHT
L.
N.
Nancy.
mor - gen mich er - freu - en Dei-ner Lie-be Gu - te Nacht! Bit-ter
pray'r of mine can move thee, Yet I wish thee sweet good night! Ere I
Wood
N.
mü - ssen wir be - reu - en, was im Leicht-sinn wir voll -
love, I first will prove thee, I would give my heart a -
Plunkett.
(to Nancy)
P.
Na! Schlaf' wohl und mag Dich reu-en, was Du
Ah, I fear, in sooth I love thee, Tho' I've
Cl. & Bssn. sust.
N.
tr
bracht. Ach! wie woll - te ich mich freu - en, hiess' es:
right; Words a - lone will nev - er move me, So good-
P.
un - ge-schickt vollbracht! Wer wird denn die Ar-beit scheu-en?
no return but spite! Why so hard-ly would you prove me?

Lady H.
Muss so bit-ter ich be-
Words like his to love might
Nancy.
Pachthof, gu-te Nacht! Gu-te Nacht, gu-te Nacht! Bit-ter müssen wir be-
bye now and good night! so good-bye and good night! Ere I love I first will
Lionel.
Gu-te Nacht! Schlafe wohl und mag Dich
Ah, good night! all good angels watch a-
Plunkett.
Wet-termädel! Gu-te Nacht, gu-te Nacht, gu-te Nacht! Na, schlaf wohl und mag Dich
Come, you Gipsy! Say good night, say good night, say good night! ah I fear in sooth I
p Str. trem.
Wind sust.
reu-en, was im Leichtsinn ich voll-bracht? ach! Hier ver-letz' ich den Ge-
move me, And I must his pas-sion slight, ah, For a-las, he's learnt to
reu-en, was im Leichtsinn wir voll-bracht, ach! Ach wie woll-te ich mich
prove thee, I would give my heart a-right, ah! Words a-lone can nev-er
reu-en, was Dein ar-ger Hohn voll-bracht, ja! O lass mor-gen mich er-
bove thee, And thy scorning put to flight, ah, Tho' no pray'r of mine can
reu-en, was Du un-geschickt voll-bracht, ja! Wer wird denn die Ar-beit
love thee, Tho' I've no re-turn but spite, ah, Why so hard-ly would you
treu-en, dort die Sit-te; gu-te Nacht, gu-te Nacht, gu-te Nacht!
love me, Oh for-get me, and good night, so good night, so good night!
freu-en, hiess' es: Pacht-hof, gu-te Nacht, gu-te Nacht, gu-te Nacht!
move me. So good-bye now, and good night, so good night, so good night!
freu-en Dei-ner Lie-be gu-te Nacht. Schla-fe wohl und
move thee, Yet I wish thee sweet good night. All good an-gels
scheu-en? Wet-ter-mä-del, gu-te Nacht, gu-te Nacht, gu-te Nacht!
prove me? Come, you Gip-sy, say good night, say good night, say good night!
Harp
Hns. sust.

L.
mag Dich reu'n, was Dein ar-ger Hohn voll-bracht, o lass morgen micher-
watch a - bove thee, And thy scorning put to flight; Tho' no pray'r of mine can
Lady H.
H.
Gu - te Nacht, gu - te Nacht, gu - te Nacht!
Now good night, now good night, ah, good night!
Nancy.
N.
Gu - te Nacht, gu - te Nacht, gu - te Nacht!
Now good night, now good night, ah, good night!
Lionel.
L.
freu - en Dei - ner Lie - be - gu - te Nacht, gu - te Nacht, gu - te Nacht!
move thee, Yet I wish thee sweet good night, now good night, ah, good night!
Plunkett.
P.
Gu - te Nacht, gu - te Nacht, gu - te Nacht!
Now good night, now good night, ah, good night!
(Plunkett locks the central door and goes out with Lionel L.H.)
Hn. Solo
Harp
f Cello & Bass
p

No. 11. Recit. and Terzettino. – „Fort von hinnen, lasst uns eilen."

(Tristram knocks at the window outside.)
H.
Ach!__ Ach!__ Ach! Was soll ge-
Ah!__ Ah!__ Ah! what can it
N.
Sturm, den nichts be-schwört. Ja, ach! Ja, ach!
more at court ap-pear. Why ah? why ah?
Str.
schehn? Grosse Götter! Hörst Du dort?
be? Gracious heaven! Do you hear?
Grosse Götter! Hören schwindet mir und
Gracious heaven! I am near-ly dead with
Lady H.
(aside)
Tris - tan! Er wird
Tristram (outside). Tris - tram! He will
Nancy. (she opens the window; Tristram enters)
T.
Seh'n! La - dy! La - dy! Ach! der Lord.
fear! La - dy Har - riet! It is he.
pp
cresc.
Tristram.
schmäh'n und ich ver-die - ne sei-nen Zorn. Ha! Un - er - hört! La - dy!
scold, and I de-serve all he can say. Mon-strous in - deed! La - dy
f
p

Nancy.
Lady H.
N.
H.
Ruhig! Stört nicht die Schläfer in der Nähe! Fort, ja
Softly, you will dis-turb the sleeping farmers! Let us
T.
La-dy! und Cou-si-ne, Eh-ren-fräu-lein!
Har-riet! Gen-tle Cou-sin! Maid of honour!
tr
H.
fort!
fly!
Lasst uns
Let us
T.
Dass man uns nicht er-spä-he, liess ich mei-nen Wa-gen steh'n, fünfzig Schritt weit.
That none may seek our trac-es, I've my car-riage waiting near, fol-low quick-ly!
H.
geh'n!
fly!
Lasst uns geh'n!
Let us fly!
Nancy.
N.
Lasst uns geh'n!
Let us fly!
Tristram.
T.
Lasst uns geh'n!
Let us fly!
f
dim.

Allegro.
H.
N.
T.
Ei - len! ei - len, husch, husch,
Haste we! haste we, hush, oh
Ei - len! ei - len, husch, husch,
Haste we! haste we, hush, oh
Fort von hin-nen, lasst uns ei - len, und ent-rin-nen oh-ne Wei - len, husch, husch,
From this spot now quickly haste we, Not an-oth-er moment waste we, Hush, oh
Allegro.
p Str. pizz.
Wood. Str.
Wood Str.
husch! sind wir hin-aus_ Le-be wohl, du friedlich Haus! Fort von hin-nen, lasst uns ei - len, und ent-
hush, and ere we fly, To this hov-el say good-bye, From this spot now quickly haste we, not an-
husch! sind wir hin-aus_ Le-be wohl, du friedlich Haus! Fort von hin-nen, lasst uns ei - len, und ent-
hush, and ere we fly, To this hov-el say good-bye, From this spot now quickly haste we, not an-
husch! sind wir hin-aus_ Le-be wohl, du nie-d'res Haus! Ei - len,
hush, and ere we fly, To this hov-el say good-bye, haste we,
arco
p Ob. Cl. & Bssn.
ritard.
rin-nen oh - ne Wei - len, husch, husch, husch! sind wir hin - aus_ Le-be wohl, du friedlich
oth-er moment waste we, hush, oh hush, and ere we fly, to this hov - el say good-
rin-nen oh - ne Wei - len, husch, husch, husch! sind wir hin - aus_ Le-be wohl, du friedlich
oth-er moment waste we, hush, oh hush, and ere we fly, to this hov - el say good-
ritard.
ei - len, husch, husch, husch! sind wir hin - aus_ Le-be wohl, du nie-d'res
haste we, hush, oh hush, and ere we fly, to this hov - el say good-
colla voce

lento
H.
Haus ah, ah, ah, le - be
bye, ah, ah, I'll say good-
N.
Haus, le-be wohl, du fried-lich Haus, le-be wohl, du friedlich Haus, le-be wohl,
bye, to this house I say good-bye, to this house I say good-bye, say good-bye,
T.
Haus, le-be wohl, du nie-d'res Haus, le-be wohl, du nie-d'res Haus, le-be wohl,
bye, to this hov-el say good-bye, to this hov-el say good-bye, say good-bye,
Str.
wohl, le-be wohl, du fried - lich Haus!
bye, to the house I'll say good-bye!
du fried-lich, fried-lich Haus, le - be wohl!
thou peace-ful house, good-bye, ah, good-bye!
le - be wohl!
say good-bye!
Ob. & Cl.
Str.
Cl. solo
pp
(Tristram places the bench for the ladies to go out by the window; silence; a sound of carriage-wheels is heard.)
p
Hns. & Bssn.
Recit.
Plunkett (within).
(enters)
P.
Na! Was soll das lan-ge Schwärmen! könnt dann Morgen nicht her-aus? Wa-gen-
Well, now long e-nough you've slumber'd, let your day be-gin be-times. What, a
cresc.
Vla.
Cello & Bass

P.
rasseln? Welch ein Lär-men! Ha das Fen-ster!_Leute, 'raus! Leu-te,
carriage? Wheels are rat-tling! Ha, the window! Peo-ple, ho! from your
Vl.
f Tutti
P.
L.
Lionel (enters L.H.).
Plunkett.
'raus! Sprich! Was gibt's denn? Die-be! Die-be! Die-be! Halt! die Mädchen_
beds! Say, what is it? Signs of thieves and bur-glars! Ha, those wenches!
p Str.
f Tutti
f Str.
P.
L.
Lionel.
Fort!_Ent-floh'n? Was! Ent-floh'n? Sie, die ich
What, they're gone! How, they've gone? She who en-
L.
lie - be?
thrall'd me?
Fort! Ihr nach! Es gilt mein
Come! a - way! pur-sue their
Plunkett.
P.
Das ist mei-ner Sanft-muth Lohn!
For your love a nice re - turn!
Vl.
p
L.
(rushes off)
Le - ben! Ihr nach! Ihr nach! Es gilt mein Le - ben!
trac-es! A-way! a - way! or let me per - ish!
f Tutti

Plunkett.
P.
Na! Mein Le-ben gilt's just nicht, doch ein Beispiel will ich
Well I'll per-ish by and bye, but just yet my life I'll
p Str.
ge - ben, wie man straft ver-letz - te Pflicht. He! Ihr Leu-te! he! Ihr
cher-ish, And those run - a - ways we'll punish! Up, a-rouse ye, all my
f Tutti
(rings the bell outside)
Chorus (some servants rushing in).
Leu - te! Was be-deu-tet das Ge-
peo - ple! What on earth can be the
f p Str.
f Tutti
p
f
läu - te? was be - deu - tet das Ge - läu - te? Ein paar Mäg-de floh'n ins
mat - ter? Why this shout-ing and this clat - ter? Our two ser-vants have ab -
Wei - te, floh'n ins Wei - te, floh'n ins Wei - te, ein Pfund Ster-ling, wer sie
scond-ed, our two ser-vants have ab - scond - ed, for their cap-ture here's a

Chorus (Servants).
Plunkett (ringing the bell).
P.
bringt. Ein Pfund Ster-ling, wer sie bringt. He! Ihr Leu-te! He! Ihr
pound. For their cap-ture here's a pound. Up, my peo-ple! up, my
p
f
Tutti
Leu-te!
peo-ple!
Chorus (other servants).
Was be-deu-tet das Ge-
What on earth can be the
p Str.
f Tutti
Plunkett.
Ein paar Mäg-de floh'n ins
Our two ser-vants have ab-
läu - te? was be - deu - tet das Ge - läu - te?
mat - ter? why this shout - ing and this clat - ter?
Wei - te, floh'n ins Wei - te, floh'n ins Wei - te, zwei Pfund, wer zu - rück sie
scond-ed, our two ser-vants have ab - scond-ed, bring them back and take two
Chorus.
(exeunt)
zwingt! Zwei Pfund, wer zu-rück sie zwingt!
pounds! Bring them back and take two pounds!
Tutti

Plunkett.
P.
Ruht nicht, bis Ihr sie ge - fun - den! Ih - nen nach auf Feld und Flur; fang' ich
Take no rest till you have caught them, seek in ev'-ry field and lane, good re -
Chorus.
Ruht nicht, bis sie ge - fun - den, ih - nen
We'll not rest till we've caught them, We will
Ruht nicht, bis sie ge - fun - den, ih - nen
We'll not rest till we've caught them, We will
ff Tutti
sie, wird sie ge - bun - den, hätt' ich sie für's Er - ste nur! Su - chet,
ward when ye have brought them, Blows if ye have seach'd in vain! Hasten,
nach auf Feld und Flur! Su - chet sie, die
seek in field and lane! You'll re - ward us
nach auf Feld und Flur! Su - chet sie, die
seek in field and lane! You'll re - ward us
bis Ihr sie ge - fun - den, fang' ich sie, wird sie ge - bun - den, hätt' ich sie für's Er - ste
rest not till you've caught them, take no rest till you have caught them, seek in ev'-ry field and
hier ver - schwun - den, su - chet der Ent - eil - ten
when we've brought them, And we will not search in
hier ver - schwun - den, su - chet der Ent - eil - ten
when we've brought them, And we will not search in

P.
nur! fang' ich sie, fang' ich sie, dann
lane, haste a - way, haste a - way, rest
Spur. Ru - het nicht, bis sie ge - fun - - den, ja,
vain. We'll not rest till we have caught them, come,
Spur. Ru - het nicht, bis sie ge - fun - - den, ja,
vain. We'll not rest, till we have caught them, come,
P.
wird sie ge - bun - den, ja, ge - bun - den, ja, ge - bun - den, dann wird sie ge-
not till you've caught them, till you've caught them, till you've caught them, rest not till you've
ih - nen nach auf Feld und Flur! Ha! Su - chet
let us seek in field and lane, come, you'll re -
ih - nen nach auf Feld und Flur! Ha! Su - chet
let us seek in field and lane, come, you'll re -
P.
bun - den, ja, ge - bun - den, ja, ge - bun - den!
caught them, till you've caught them, till you've caught them!
sie, die hier ent - schwun - den, su - chet der Ent - eil - ten
ward us when we've brought them, and we will not search in
sie, die hier ent - schwun - den, su - chet der Ent - eil - ten
ward us when we've brought them, and we will not search in

P.
Hätt' ich sie nur!
Search not in vain!
Spur, der Ent - eil - ten Spur!
vain, we'll not search in vain!
Spur, der Ent - eil - ten Spur!
vain, we'll not search in vain!
8
P.
ff
Wind
Tutti
K-dr.

End of Act II.

Act III.

A wood. Small inn, L. H., before which Plunkett and farmers are seated at a table.

Nº 12. Entr'acte and Song. _ „Lasst mich euch fragen."

Flute, Piccolo, Oboes, Clarinets in C, Bassoons, Horns in F & C, Trumpets in F, Trombones, Ophicleide, Kettledrums in F & C, Big Drum & Strings.

Andante maestoso.
Plunkett.
P.
Lasst mich euch fra-gen, könnt ihr mir sa-gen, was un-serm Land, der Brit - ten
Search the world o - ver, Can you dis - co-ver Why does the Bri - ton beat his
p Str.
Strand, die wah - re Kraft schafft, he? Das ist das kräft'-ge E - li -
foes by land and wa - ter, Eh? That is be - cause his drink is
f
Ob.
p
Str. & Hns.
xir, das ist das säft - ge Por - ter - bier, das regt John Bull im Ne - bel -
beer, That is the best of all good cheer, John Bull can fight And guard his
Fl. & Picc.
dampf, zu Meer und Land, beim Bo-xer - kampf. Ja! Hur-
right, In bat - tle's roar He's to the fore. Ha, Hur-
lento
f Tutti
ff
rah, dem Hop-fen, Hur-rah, dem Malz, sie sind des Da - seins Würz' und Salz, Hur-
rah, I'll sing of the glo-rious malt, The best of drinks 'neath yon blue vault. Hur-
p Wind & Str.

P.
rah, tra la la la la la la la, Hurrah! Könnt ihr er-gründen, soll ich euch
rah, tra la la la la la la la, Hurrah! Here is a question For your sug-
Chorus.
TENOR.
Hurrah!
Hurrah!
BASS.
Hurrah!
Hurrah!
f Tutti
Str.
ff Tutti
p Str.
kün-den, was unsre Brust er-füllt mit Lust bis fro - her Sang klang, he? Das ist der
gestion When we re-joice With lus-ty voice, What strength in-spires us, Eh? Why, 'tis the
Ob.
f
p
Brau-ne hier im Krug, der hebt die Lau-ne Zug für Zug, das ist das her - be, der - be
tankard foaming high, Dullness and care be-fore it fly, Give me a draught of En-glish
Str. & Hns.
Fl. & Picc.
lento
tr
Nass, das ist das Bier, ja, das giebt den Bass. Ha, Hur-rah! dem Hopfen, hur-
beer, I'll brave the world nor know aught of fear. Ha, Hur-rah, I'll sing of the
f Tutti
ff
p Wind & Str.

P.
rah! dem Malz, sie sind des Le - bens Würz und Salz, hur-rah! — tra la la la la la la
glo-rious malt, The best of drinks 'neath yon blue vault, hur-rah, — tra la la la la la la
f Tutti
Str.
la, Hur-rah, hur-rah! dem Por-ter-bier, dem Por-ter - bier, hur-rah, hur-
la, Hur-rah, hur-rah! for En-glish beer, for En-glish - beer hur-rah, hur-
Chorus.
Hur-rah, hur-rah! dem Por-ter-bier, dem Por-ter - bier, hurrah, hur-
Hur-rah, hur-rah for En-glish beer, for En-glish beer, hurrah, hur-
Hur-rah, hur-rah! dem Por-ter-bier, dem Por-ter - bier, hurrah, hur-
Hur-rah, hur-rah for En-glish beer, for En-glish beer, hurrah, hur-
Tutti
rah dem Por-ter-bier, dem Por - ter - bier, hur-rah!
rah for En-glish-beer, for En - glish - beer, hur-rah!
rah dem Por-ter-bier, dem Por - ter - bier, hur-rah!
rah for En-glish beer, for En - glish beer, hur-rah!
rah dem Por-ter-bier, dem Por - ter - bier, hur-rah!
rah for En-glish beer, for En - glish beer, hur-rah!
ff

No 13. Chorus.—„Auch wir Frau'n, wir kennen."

Schö - nen.
la - dies.
Na! so lauft, ich will erst
Go, I first will pay the
Kommt doch, kommt, die Hör - ner schal - len!
Look, their plumes are gai - ly beck-'ning!
(Exeunt Chorus R. H.)
Kommt doch, kommt, die Hör - ner schal - len!
Look, their plumes are gai - ly beck-'ning!
f Tutti
Hns. (on the stage)
(exit into inn)
(Enter Nancy with Chorus of Huntresses.)
zah - len.
reck - 'ning.
p Str. & Wind (Orchestra)
cresc.
SOPRANO.
Auch wir Frau'n, wir ken - nen, traun! das
Ah, we mai - dens know full well the
ALTO.
Auch wir Frau'n, wir ken - nen, traun! das
Ah, we mai - dens know full well the
f Tutti
f Hns. (on the stage)
Sas - sa, hus - sa! Tra la la la! Bil - den oh - ne Müh' zur Jagd uns
ho, tal - ly ho, tra la la la! No - ble game we hunt with wile and
Sas - sa, hus - sa! Tra la la la! Bil - den oh - ne Müh' zur Jagd uns
ho, tal - ly ho, tra la la la! No - ble game we hunt with wile and

früh! Ha la li, ha la la li! Die Herrn Jä - ger sel - ber sind das
spell, Ha la li, ha la la li! Each pur - sues her cho - sen lord With
früh! Ha la li, ha la la li! Die Herrn Jä - ger sel - ber sind das
spell, Ha la li, ha la la li! Each pur - sues her cho - sen lord With
Wild, dem es gilt, lis - tig ge - zielt; und die Au - gen blit - zen als Ge-
glance and with word, sharp-er than sword; From the ar - rows of her eye the
Wild, dem es gilt, lis - tig ge - zielt; und die Au - gen blit - zen als Ge-
glance and with word, sharp-er than sword; From the ar - rows of her eye the
schoss da-rauf los, feu - rig d'rauf los. Bald sie scheu-chen, dass sie wei - chen,
shaft she lets fly, none may come nigh. Now we scare them, While we dare them,
schoss da-rauf los, feu - rig d'rauf los. Bald sie scheu-chen, dass sie wei - chen,
shaft she lets fly, none may come nigh. Now we scare them, While we dare them,
Str. & Wind in the Orchestra added
bald si hä - gen, treu - los pfle - gen, bald sie het - zen zu den Net - zen,
Then we please them While we tease them, Now re-lent - ing, Then re - pent - ing,
bald si hä - gen, treu - los pfle - gen, bald sie het - zen zu den Net - zen,
Then we please them While we tease them, Now re-lent - ing, Then re - pent - ing,

bis in Schlin-gen sie sich fin-gen, das ist so die Lieb-lings-jagd, die den Frau-en
Our be-hests there's no re-sent-ing, Thus the mer-ry chase goes on Till the no-ble
bis in Schlin - gen sie sich fin-gen, das ist so die Lieb-lings-jagd, die den Frau-en
Our be-hests there's no re-sent-ing, Thus the mer-ry chase goes on Till the no-ble
stets be-hagt, das ist so die Lieb-lings-jagd, die den Frau-en be-
game is won, Thus the mer-ry chase goes on, Till the game we have
stets be-hagt, das ist so die Lieb - lings-jagd, die den Frau-en be-
game is won, Thus the mer-ry chase goes on, Till the game we have
hagt! Tra ra, tra ra, tra ra, ta ta ta, tra ra, tra ra, tra ra, ta ta
won! Tra ra, tra ra, tra ra, ta ta ta, tra ra, tra ra, tra ra, ta ta
hagt! Tra ra, tra ra, tra ra, ta ta ta, tra ra, tra ra, tra ra, ta ta
won! Tra ra, tra ra, tra ra, ta ta ta, tra ra, tra ra, tra ra, ta ta
ta, tra ra, tra ra, tra ra, tra ra, ra!
ta, tra ra, tra ra, tra ra, tra ra, ra!
ta, tra ra, tra ra, tra ra, tra ra, ra!
ta, tra ra, tra ra, tra ra, tra ra, ra!
ff Tutti

No 14. Song.* – „Jägerin, schlau im Sinn."

Allegro non troppo.
f Tutti
p Wind
Hns. & Bssn.
Nancy.
1. Jä-ge-rin, schlau im Sinn, zie-let mit den Bli-cken, weiss in Eil',
2. Süsser Schmerz traf das Herz, mit dem gold'nen Pfei-le, jetzt geschwind
1. Huntress fair, Lay your snare In be-witch-ing glances, While the dart
2. When with pain Well-nigh slain, At your feet he's su-ing, With a smile
Vl.
Pfeil auf Pfeil aus dem Aug' zu schi-cken, oh-ne Ruh' im-mer-zu,
Bal-sam lind, dass die Wun-de hei-le; seht, ein Blick bringt zu-rück
Wounds the heart, Still the pain en-tranc-es. When they sue, Still pursue,
Quick be-guile Him that's hum-bly woo-ing. Ne'er re-veal What you feel,
wacht sie un-ver-dros-sen, lau-ert schlau, zielt ge-nau, bis das Wild ge-
was ein Blick ge-nom-men, Kraft und Muth, Le-bens-glut sind aufs Neu' ge-
Till they're track'd to cov-er, Swift take aim, Seize your game, Then the contest's
Leave him still to lan-guish, Naught but woe Shall he know, Sweet is lov-er's
schos - - - - - - - sen! A-mor, das ver-schmitz-te Kind,
kom - - - - - - - men! A-mor, das ver-schmitz-te Kind,
o - - - - - - - ver! Cu-pid is a wa-ry child,
an - - - - - - - guish. Cu-pid is a wa-ry child,
tr
Wind
Str.

 * See page 247

N.
trug den Pfeil, wie der Wind, A-mor trug den Pfeil ge-schwind, wie der
lud nur blind, lud nur blind, A-mor, das ver-schmitz-te Kind, lud nur
From a-loft Guides the shaft, Cu-pid sits a-loft And guides ev-'ry
Full of smiles, Full of guiles, Ah, young Cu-pid's full of smiles and of
Wind, A-mor, das verschmitzte Kind, trug den Pfeil, wie der Wind,
blind, A-mor, das verschmitzte Kind, lud nur blind lud nur blind,
shaft, Cu-pid is a wa-ry child, From a-loft Guides the shaft,
guiles, Cu-pid is a wa-ry child, Full of smiles, Full of guiles,
Chorus.
SOPRANO.
p
Ja, A-mor, das ver-schmitz-te Kind, es trug den Pfeil ge-schwind, ge-schwind, ja, A-mor
Ja, A-mor, das ver-schmitz-te Kind, es lud nur blind, es lud nur blind, ja, A-mor,
Yes, Cu-pid is a wa-ry child, He sits a-loft And guides the shaft, yes, Cu-pid
Yes, Cu-pid is a wa-ry child, He's full of smiles And full of guiles, yes, Cu-pid
ALTO.
p
Ja, A-mor, das ver-schmitz-te Kind, es trug den Pfeil ge-schwind, ge-schwind, ja, A-mor
Ja, A-mor, das ver-schmitz-te Kind, es lud nur blind, es lud nur blind, ja, A-mor,
Yes, Cu-pid is a wa-ry child, He sits a-loft And guides the shaft, yes, Cu-pid
Yes, Cu-pid is a wa-ry child, He's full of smiles And full of guiles, yes, Cu-pid
N.
f
1.
2.
A-mor trug den Pfeil ge-schwind, wie der Wind.
A-mor, das verschmitz-te Kind, lud nur blind.
Cu-pid sits a-loft, and guides ev-'ry shaft.
ah, young Cu-pid's full of smiles and of guiles.
f
trug den Pfeil ge-schwind, ge-schwind, wie der Wind.
das ver-schmitz-te Kind, ha, ha! lud nur blind.
is a wa-ry child, and guides ev-'ry shaft.
is a wa-ry child, ha, ha! full of guiles.
f
trug den Pfeil ge-schwind, ge-schwind wie der Wind.
das ver-schmitz-te Kind, ha, ha! lud nur blind.
is a wa-ry child, and guides ev-'ry shaft.
is a wa-ry child, ha, ha! full of guiles.
1.
2.
f Tutti
p
f
p
Hns. & Bssn.
f

Allegro non troppo.
ff Tutti
(Plunkett comes out from the inn.)
f
Cello & Bass
Vl.
Plunkett.
P.
Blitz! die wil-de Jagd, für-wahr, ger-ne zähmt' ich mir ein Paar!
So, here's game in-deed! By Jove, I would tame a brace of these!
p Str.
Vl.
dolce
Hns. sustain
Nancy (aside).
N.
Wo nur mag die Her-rin wei-len? Ach? sie flieht
Where is La-dy Har-riet wand'ring? Sports no more
N.
der Freun-de Reih'n, kei-ne Freu-de will sie thei-len,
her heart can please, Ev-er lone-ly she is pon-d'ring

N.
seit an jenem Unglücks-tage sie
since that luck-less day at Rich-mond, When
Ihn sah. He! Gut Freund! sa-ge er uns doch Mein Gott!
she met My good man, Tell me, if you can Oh! Heav'n!
(perceives Plunkett)
(recognizes him and starts)
1st Vl.
2nd Vl. & Vla.
Str.
Plunkett.
Potz Blitz, Ju-li-a mit Jagd-ge-schütz!
What, you? Ju-lia, here in hunt-ing guise?
Nancy.
Gu-ter Freund Dein
My good friend Good
Più mosso
Str.
P.
N.
Freund? mit nich-ten! der Herr Rich-ter soll Dich
friend? Ex-cuse me! Not a-gain shall you a-
rich-ten; wart', ich will Dich durch-geh'n leh-ren.
buse me; Let the Sher-iff judge be-tween us.

Nancy.
Plunkett.
Nancy
Plunkett.
Nancy.
N.
P.
Ihr seid toll! Hier hilft kein Wehren! fort nach Hause. Helft, her-bei! Lose Magd! Ver-weg'-ner
Are you mad? I'll teach you how to run a-way, Miss. Hush, no more. Saucy wench! Bold man, be-
f Str. & Wind
ritard.
Mann, ver-weg'-ner Mann! Jä-ge-rin-nen, zielt! legt an! er ist Wild! die Jagd ist
gone, nor breathe my name! Let each hun-tress bold take aim! Let's bring down this boorish
Str.
ritard.
Allegretto.
frei!
game!
Chorus (pointing their spears and closing round him).
SOPRANO.
An dem Fre-chen lasst uns rä-chen, er ist das Wild, dem es hier gilt,
We will chase him, We will trace him! Who of our spears Is with-out fears?
ALTO.
An dem Fre-chen lasst uns rä-chen, er ist das Wild, dem es hier gilt,
We will chase him, We will trace him! Who of our spears Is with-out fears?
Allegretto.
ff Tutti (Orchestra, & Hns. on the stage)
ihn zu ja-gen, ihn zu pla-gen, sei un-ser Ziel, sei un-ser Spiel.
We'll pur-sue him, We'll un-do him, Till he must yield; Ours is the field!
ihn zu ja-gen, ihn zu pla-gen, sei un-ser Ziel, sei un-ser Spiel.
We'll pur-sue him, We'll un-do him, Till he must yield; Ours is the field!

Plunkett.
P.
Al - le Tausend, das wird grausend, wie die scharfen Waf-fen blit - zen, ih-re Spee-re,
They're up-on me They've undone me, 'pon my word, this game is se - rious; this is fright ful,
An dem Fre - chen lasst uns rä - chen, er ist das
We will chase him, We will trace him! Who of our
An dem Fre - chen lasst uns rä - chen, er ist das
We will chase him, We will trace him! Who of our
fühl, auf Eh - re, ich schon tief im Her - zen sit - zen, das ist ei - ne
they are spiteful, Yet there is a charm mys-te-rious, in these pret - ty
Wild, dem es hier gilt, dem es hier gilt, ihn zu
spears Is with - out fears, is with - out fears? We'll pur -
Wild, dem es hier gilt, dem es hier gilt, ihn zu
spears Is with - out fears, is with - out fears? We'll pur -
Vl.
Hns.
Teu - fels-jagd! Ei da bleib, wem es behagt, das ist ei - ne
de - mons' eyes: I'll be off, and thus be wise, I'll be off, and
ja - gen, ihn zu pla - gen, sei un - ser
sue him, We'll un - do him, Till he must
ja - gen, ihn zu pla - gen, sei un - ser
sue him, We'll un - do him, Till he must
Hns.
Vl.
Cello

P.
Teu - fels-jagd! Ei, da bleib, wem's be-hagt, ei-ne Teu - fels-
thus be wise, I'll be off, and be wise, yes, I will be
Ziel, ja! ja, es sei un-ser Spiel! Tra ra, tra ra, tra ra, ta ta
yield, Ours, ah yes, ours is the field! Tra la, tra la, tra la la la
Tutti
Hns.
jagd, ei-ne Teu - fels-jagd, ha, ha! o weh! ach, ach! o
off, yes, I will be off, ha, ha, oh me, a - las, a -
ta, tra ra, tra ra, tra ra, ta ta ta, tra ra, tra ra, tra ra, tra
la, tra la, tra la, tra la la la la, tra la, tra la, tra la, tra
(runs away, pursued by the ladies)
weh!
las!
ra ra!
la la!

Andante.
(Lionel enters, dejectedly, gazing on the flowers of Martha.)
Lionel.
Darum pflück'ich, o - Ro-se, vom Stam-me dich ab, sollst ruh'n - mir am Herzen, und mit mir, - ja, mit mir - im Grab.
I'll not leave thee, thou lone one, to - pine - on the stem, thus kind - ly I scat-ter thy - leaves o'er the bed, - a-las!
Cl.
p
Hns. & Bssn.
Vl. pizz.
Recit.
Wo war ich? ach, bei Ihr! Nur stets ihr Bild al - lein, das mir vor Au-gen strahlt mit lo-ckend hellem Schein; das mir die Brust er-füllt, mich tödtet und be-lebt, zur off'nen Gruft mich zieht, und hoch zum Himmel hebt!
Where am I? ah, I dreamt I saw her fai - ry form, her voice so sweet and low was whisp'ring near my heart; Me-thought, on me she smil'd, The bliss of Heav'n was mine! Why am I thus be-guil'd! Why must I ev - er pine?
Str. arco
Fl. & Ob.

№ 15. Song. _ „Ach! so fromm, ach so traut.“

Allegro moderato.
Fl. & Cl.
tr
p
Bssn. & Hns. sustain
Cl.
Str.
Ob.
Wind
Lionel.
Ach! so _ fromm, ach _ so _
None so _ rare, None so _
Str.
p Str.
traut, hat _ mein Au _ ge sie _ er - schaut; ach! so _ mild
fair, Yet _ en - rap-tur'd mor - tal _ heart; Maid-en _ dear,
und so _ rein drang ihr Bild _ in's Herz mir ein. _ Banger Gram, eh' sie
Past com-pare, Ah, 'twas death _ from thee to part! _ Ere I saw thy sweet
Fl.
dolce
Str.

kam, hat die Zu-kunft mir um-hüllt, doch mit ihr blüh-te mir neu-es Da-sein lust-er-
face On my heart there was no trace Of that love from a-bove That in sor-row now I
füllt. Weh! es schwand, was ich fand, ach! mein Glück erschaut' ich kaum, bin er wacht und die
prove; But, a-las, thou art gone, And in grief I mourn a-lone; Life a shad-ow doth
Nacht raub-te mir den sü-ssen Traum, den sü-ssen Traum.
seem, And my joy a fleet-ing dream, a fleet-ing dream.
dimin.
Ach! so fromm, ach so traut, hat mein Au-ge sie-er-
None so rare, None so fair, Yet en-rap-tur'd mor-tal
p
schaut. Ach! so mild und so rein drang ihr Bild in's Herz mir
heart; Maid-en dear, Past com-pare, Ah, 'twas death from thee to
ad lib.
cresc. Wind sustain
decresc.
colla voce

più animato
L.
ein. Mar - tha! Mar - tha! du ent-schwandest, und mein
part. Mar - tha! Mar - tha! I con - jure thee, Leave me
più animato
mf
Glück nahmst Du mit Dir; gib mir wie - der, was Du
not to lone de - spair; Leave me scathe - less, I im -
fan - dest, o - der thei - le es mit mir, ja!
plore thee, Or re - turn, my life to share, Oh,
cresc.
f Tutti
(Throws himself on a bank of turf and remains absorbed.)
thei - le es mit mir, ja! mit mir.
come, my life to share, ah, re - turn!
ff più animato
8
p

No 16. Recit. and Finale – „Hier in stillen Schattengründen.“

(Same Score.)

(Enter Lady Harriet and Tristram, at the back; Lionel is turned away from them.)

Allegretto.
p Str. & Wind
Recit. Tristram.
Die Her-rin ras-tet dort, wes-halb ent-fernt ihr Euch von der Mo-
Her Ma-jes-ty's gone on, why have you left your post to muse in
Str.
Lady H.
narchin? Um al-lein zu sein.
silence? I would be a-lone.
Tristram (tenderly). Mit mir?
With me?
Lady H.
Mit Euch? Je nun, es gilt mir
With you? No diff'rence can I
gleich. Seid Ihr, Mylord, mit mir, fühl' ich mich ganz al-lein.
find; If you are here or not, I'm sure I do not mind.
p Str. & Wind
Tristram.
Stets trau-rig?
Why sorr'wing?
Lady H.
Geht denn, und flie-het mei-ne Nä-he.
Pray go, and spare me fur-ther comments.
Tristram.
Nicht
Nay,

Lady H.
Tristram.
Moderato.
(exit)
T.
H.
doch, im Wald al - lein? So will ich's! Fort! Ich ge - he.
nay, in this dark wood_ O - bey me! Go! I leave you.
Str.
Ob. Hns. & Bssn.
Lady H.
Hier in stil - len Schat - ten - grün - den, in _ dem ein - sam
In these syl - van dark re - cess - es, Where_ the night - in -
Cl.
Str. pizz.
trau - ten Hain, hier darf frei das Herz sich kün - den sein_Ver - lan - gen, sei - ne Pein,
gales complain, Here the ach - ing heart ex - press - es All _ its long - ing, all its pain,
Ob. & Cl.
Wind
sein Ver - lan - gen, sei - ne Pein, sein Ver - lan - gen, sei - ne Pein, sei - ne
all its long - ing, all its pain, all its long - ing, all its pain, all its
Pein. Was es füh - let, was es lei - det, still _ be - kennt und
pain. All that deep with - in is trea - sur'd, Though_ the tongue its

H.
laut verhöhnt, wen es suchet, ach! und meidet, wen es schmäht und
spell deny, Here asserts its pow'r unmeasur'd, And the heart makes
Ob. & Cl.
doch ersehnt, wen es schmäht und doch ersehnt, wen es
fond reply, and the heart makes fond reply, and the
Wind
Str.
schmäht und doch ersehnt, und doch er - sehnt.
heart makes fond reply, makes fond re - ply.
Allegro.
Lionel (perceiving, starts).
Diese Stimme
Heav'n, those accents
Vl.
p
Str.
Cello & Bass
Lady H. (recognizing him).
Götter!
Heaven,
Ha! was seh' ich! eine Dame
Ha, amazement! but a lady
(aside)
Er! Wie entgeh' ich dieser Angst?
he? Ah, how can I fly from hence?
(in great agitation)
Martha! Martha! Du kamst
Martha! Martha! Thou art

L.
her? Hab' Dank, ich seh' Dich wie-der! Ja, Du
here? Oh, thanks for thy re-turn-ing! Ah, 'tis
Cl. & Bssn. sustain
L.
H.
Lady H.
Lionel.
bist's, die mir entschwand! (Fassung!) Blickst so stolz her-
thou! I've waited long! (Courage!) Why those haugh-ty
cresc.
L.
nie-der? Hat mein Herz dich doch er-kannt.
glanc-es? Ah, my heart di-vined thee here!
ff Tutti
Lady H.
Lionel.
H.
L.
Mich erkannt? Ihr irrt. O nimmer schwand Dein Bild aus meiner
You mistake, good sir. I knew thee at a glance, I'm not de-
Str. & Wind
L.
Brust, nein, mich täuscht nicht die-ser Schim-mer, Du
ceiv'd, yes, I care not for thy splen-dors, 'tis

Lady H.
Lionel.
bist's, Du! mir ist's be-wusst! Thor, Ihr träumt! Ha! wär' es
thou, thou! my love-ly maid! Go, you dream! Ha! if I'm
Träu-men, das um-strah-let mei-nen Blick, wohl denn,
dream-ing, Let me nev-er-more a-wake! With thine
ff Tutti
p Str.
Mar-tha! oh-ne Säu-men fas-se ich mein kur-zes
eyes up-on me beam-ing, Let me live for thy sweet
Lady H.
Fort! hinweg!
Hush, no more!
(attempts to take her hand)
Glück. Nein, nein, ich träu-me! Träu-mend halt' ich dei-ne
sake! I would be dream-ing that I hold thy hand in
(kneels at her feet)
Hand, küss' im süssen Wahn die Säu-me von dem glän-zen-den Ge-wand.
mine, That in bliss I kiss thy garment's hem, and breathe thy breath di-vine!
f Tutti

Lady H. (repelling him).
Ha! Vermess'ner, schon zu lange hört' ich, was dein Irrsinn spricht!
Hence, au-dacious man, I warn thee! Si-lence, hasten from this spot!
Nein, ich sprach aus Herzens-drange.
Gen-tle heart, thou wilt not scorn me.
Fre-cher Knecht, ich kenn euch nicht!
Base-born churl, I know thee not!
(springs to his feet)
Knecht! Knecht! Verweg'-ne!
Churl, churl! and baseborn!
Dein Ge-bie-ter bin ich, Dein Herr, dem Du zu-ge-sagt; war ich mild und schwach als Hü-ter, jetzt er-zit-tre, nie-d're Magd!
Cease that in-so-lent tone, no more dare my will gain-say; I have hir'd thee for my ser-vant, thou thy mas-ter shalt o-bey!
colla parte
Lady H. (in great terror).
Tris-tan, Tris-tan! Hül-fe! ret-tet!
Tris-tram, Tris-tram! Help, oh help me!
a tempo
Str.
Tristram.
Was begehrt Ihr? Ha, wer wagt?
Do you call me? Who has dared?
(enters)
cresc.
f & Wind

Lionel. ad lib.
L.
Ich, ihr Herr! Ver-ge-bens wehrt ihr meinem Recht, mein ist die Magd, — mein ist die
Dared? 'twas I! let none presume my right t'as-sail; this is my ser vant hir'd by
colla parte
ff Tutti
Tristram.
L. H.
Magd! Ha! der Frech-heit oh - ne Glei - chen, Dei - nen Fre - vel lohn' ich
law. Ha! this boor is too au - da - cious, Such a case I nev - er
Allegro non troppo.
p Str. Bssn. & Hns.
T.
Dir! Stra - fe soll Dich Thor er - rei - chen! Her! Ihr Leu - te, her zu
saw! Cease to urge this claim men - da - cious, Ho! ye peo - ple, hold him
T.
(Enter Chorus.)
mir, her zu mir!
fast! Hold him fast!
f
Brass
Chorus.
SOPRANO.
TENOR.
Welch ein Lär - men oh - ne Glei - chen in der Für - stin Jagd - re - vier,
Whence this quar - rel and con - fu - sion, Dare ye, in the Roy - al Park?
BASS.
Welch ein Lär - men oh - ne Glei - chen in der Für - stin Jagd - re - vier,
Whence this quar - rel and con - fu - sion, Dare ye, in the Roy - al Park?
Wind
fp
'Cello & Bass.

Stra - fe soll den Thor er - rei - chen, stö - ret er die Freu - de hier.
Hence a - way, or thy in - tru - sion For our spears shall be the mark.
Stra - fe soll den Thor er - rei - chen, stö - ret er die Freu - de hier.
Hence a - way, or thy in - tru - sion For our spears shall be the mark.
Welch ein Lärmen oh - ne Glei - chen in der Fürstin Jagd - re - vier,
Whence this quar - rel and con - fu - sion, Dare ye, in the Roy - al Park?
Welch ein Lär - men oh - ne Glei - chen in der Für - stin Jagd - re - vier,
Whence this quar - rel and con - fu - sion, Dare ye, in the Roy - al Park?
Welch ein Lär - men oh - ne Glei - chen in der Für - stin Jagd - re - vier,
Whence this quar - rel and con - fu - sion, Dare ye, in the Roy - al Park?
Vl.
Wind
Stra - fe soll den Thor er - rei - chen, stö - ret er die Freu - de hier.
Hence a - way, or thy in - tru - sion For our spears shall be the mark.
Stra - fe soll den Thor er - rei - chen, stö - ret er die Freu - de hier.
Hence a - way, or thy in - tru - sion For our spears shall be the mark.
Stra - fe soll den Thor er - rei - chen, stö - ret er die Freu - de hier.
Hence a - way, or thy in - tru - sion For our spears shall be the mark.
cresc.

Lady H.
Ha! der Fol - ter
Ha! too cru - el
Lionel.
Ha! der Frech - heit
Ha! is't dream - ing
Tristram.
Ha! der Frechheit oh - ne Glei - chen, dei - nen Fre - vel lohn' ich dir, der
Cease, thou oaf, thy vile de - lu - sion, Or our spear-heads thou shalt mark, quick
Ha! welch Lär - men oh - ne Glei - chen in der Für - stin Jagd - re - vier, welch
Cease, thou oaf, thy vile de - lu - sion, Or our spear-heads thou shalt mark, quick,
Tutti ff
oh - ne Glei - chen, hart straft sich
his il - lu - sion, Un - kind Fate,
oh - ne Glei - chen, ich er - kenn'
or il - lu - sion? Un - kind Fate,
Frechheit oh - ne Gleichen, dei - nen Fre - vel lohn' ich dir, ja! Stra - fe soll dich
cease thy vile de - lu - sion, or our spear-heads thou shalt mark, hence, or our spear-heads,
Lär - men oh - ne Gleichen in der Für - stin Jagd - re - vier, ja! Stra - fe soll den
cease thy vile de - lu - sion, or our spear-heads thou shalt mark, hence, or our spear-heads,

H.
mein Leichtsinn hier, Spott und Hohn wird
am I thy mark? Ah, my brain is
L.
Euch, Gau-kler Ihr, Eu'-rem Tru-ge
am I thy mark? Ah, my brain is
T.
Thor er-rei-chen, her, ihr Leu-te, her zu mir! Stra-fe soll den
or our spear-heads, or our spear-heads thou shalt mark! Cease, thou oaf, thy
Thor, ja Stra-fe soll den Thor er-rei-chen, stö-ret er die Freu-de, stö-ret
thou shalt mark! no quar-rel or con-fu-sion must disgrace the Roy-al Park, dis-
Thor, ja Stra-fe soll den Thor er-rei-chen, stö-ret er die Freu-de, stö-ret
thou shalt mark! no quar-rel or con-fu-sion must disgrace the Roy-al Park, dis-
Thor, ja Stra-fe soll den Thor er-rei-chen, stö-ret er die Freu-de, stö-ret
thou shalt mark! no quar-rel or con-fu-sion must disgrace the Roy-al Park, dis-
H.
mich er-rei-chen, weh mir Ar-men, we-he
in con-fu-sion, All is er-ror, all is
L.
sollt' ich wei-chen? Kei-ne Macht ent-reisst sie
in con-fu-sion, All is er-ror, all is
T.
Thor er-rei-chen, stö-ret er die Freu-de
vile de-lu-sion, Or our spear-heads thou shalt
er die Freu-de hier, ja, stö-ret er die Freu-de, stö-ret er die Freu-de
grace the Roy-al Park, hence, hence, thou oaf, no quar-rel must dis-grace the Roy-al
er die Freu-de hier, ja, stö-ret er die Freu-de, stö-ret er die Freu-de
grace the Roy-al Park, hence, hence, thou oaf, no quar-rel must dis-grace the Roy-al
er die Freu-de hier, ja, stö-ret er die Freu-de, stö-ret er die Freu-de
grace the Roy-al Park, hence, hence, thou oaf, no quar-rel must dis-grace the Roy-al

H.
mir, weh mir Ar-men, we-he mir!
dark, all is er-ror, all is dark!
L.
mir, kei-ne Macht entreisst sie mir!
dark, all is er-ror, all is dark!
Plunkett.
T.
P.
hier, her ihr Freun-de, her zu mir! Sprich, was
mark, or our spear-heads thou shalt mark! Who are
hier, stö-ret er die Freu-de hier.
Park, must dis-grace the Roy-al Park.
hier, stö-ret er die Freu-de hier.
Park, must dis-grace the Roy-al Park.
hier, stö-ret er die Freu-de hier.
Park, must dis-grace the Roy-al Park.
Lionel.
Nancy.
L.
N.
Hilf mir, Freund! Was geht hier
Stand by me! What does this
Plunkett.
P.
giebt's? was ist ge-scheh'n?
these? why all this noise?
f
Str. p
Lionel (perceiving Nancy).
Nancy (hastening to Lady Harriet).
N.
L.
vor? Ha, auch sie! Was muss ich seh'n? La-dy?
mean? Ju-lia too! You here, my la-dy? Ma-dam!
P.
Wie-der sie! wie-der sie!
Here a-gain! here a-gain!

Lionel (abashed).
Più lento.
L.
La-dy! O, ich Thor Nur ein Spiel, was sie ge-trie-ben,
La-dy! ah, I see! 'Twas a jest she play'd up-on me!
p Str. Hns. sustain
nur ein sünd-haft Gau-kel-spiel, ih-re Zau-ber-macht zu
When she seem'd as kind as fair, Now she flies when she's un-
Tristram.
L. T.
ü-ben, o, zu viel der Schmach, zu viel! Die-sen
done me, Ah, 'tis more than I can bear! Bind this
ff Tutti
Lionel. Lady H.
L. H.
Bin-den mich? O her-be Pein.
Touch me not! Oh, I shall die!
Plunkett. Nancy.
T. P. N.
Wahn-be-thör-ten bindet! Bin-den ihn? O her-be Pein.
mad-man straight in fetters! Touch him not! Oh, I shall die!
ff
Lady H.
H.
Um Gott halt ein!
Oh hush, no more!
Lionel. Nancy.
L. N.
Hört erst, was mein Wort ver-kündet: Die-se kam Halt ein!
First hear what in truth I tell ye, these two maids No more!
p Str

Lionel (not heeding them).
zu be-thö-ren mei-nen Sinn, — in mein Haus als Die - ne-
For my ser-vice I en-gaged — them to ply for law - ful
Wind
Lady H.
Ha, ha, ha, ha, ha, ha, ha,
Nancy. Ha, ha, ha, ha, ha, ha, ha,
rin.
wage.
Ha, ha, ha, ha, ha, ha, ha,
Ha, ha, ha, ha, ha, ha, ha,
Chorus.
Wie?
How?
Wie?
How?
Wie?
How?
ff Tutti
p Wood
ha!
ha! Tristram.
Doch sein Un - glück heischt Er-
On this mad - man have com-
ha! Ha, ha, ha, ha, ha, ha, ha, ha!
ha! Ha, ha, ha, ha, ha, ha, ha, ha!
Ha, ha, ha, ha, ha, ha, ha, ha!
Ha, ha, ha, ha, ha, ha, ha, ha!
Ha, ha, ha, ha, ha, ha, ha, ha!
Ha, ha, ha, ha, ha, ha, ha, ha!
Ha, ha, ha, ha, ha, ha, ha, ha!
Ha, ha, ha, ha, ha, ha, ha, ha!
Vl.
pp
Ophicl. Cello & Bass

H.
barmen, Mit-leid sei uns heil'-ge Pflicht, mil-de Haft ver-
passion, The be-night-ed pit-y crave; What he said in
gönnt dem Ar-men, Wahn-sinn ist's, der aus ihm
ab-er-ra-tion, From my heart I long for-
H. L.N. P.T.
Lionel.
Nancy.
Plunkett (tries to make his way to Lionel).
Tristram (gives a sign that Plunkett is to hold aloof).
spricht. O des Frevels! Ach! der Arme! Hört auch mich! Zurück mit
gave. Vile as-sumption! What a pit-y! Hear me speak! Be si-lent,
Chorus.
ff
Wahn-sinn, Wahn-sinn!
Ah, 'tis mad-ness!
ff Tutti
p Str.
T. L.
Jenem!
fellow!
Cl. & Bssn.
Lionel.
Mag der
Ah, may
p
Ped.
'Cello, Bass & K.-dr.

Nº 17. Quintet – „Mag der Himmel Euch vergeben.“

H.
that — im Ü - ber-muth?
hope — I could de-stroy?
N.
muth, — im Ü - ber-muth?
stroy, — she could de-stroy?
L.
trü - ber Zu-kunft Nacht. — To-des - schmerz — hat mich ge-
life — thou couldst de - stroy! — Mor-tal pangs — my bo-som
T.
muth, — der Ü - ber-muth?
noy, — their deep an - noy?
P.
muth, — im Ü - ber-muth?
story, — she could de-stroy?
Chorus.
pp
Was nur hat sich hier be - ge - ben, hat sich hier be -
Thou shalt find we'll not re - prieve thee, we will not re -
Oh.
Wind sustain
L.
trof - fen, Dank Euch, Dank, — die es — voll - bracht, — Dank Euch,
rend - ing, By thy cru - el — hands were giv'n, — by thy
ge - ben? Straft des Knechtes, straft des Knech-tes Ü - ber-muth, straft des
prieve thee, Hence, dis-turb-er, hence, dis-turb - er of our joy, hence, dis -

Lady H.
H.
p cresc.
ff
Ach! Ach! kann der
Ah! Ah! Ah, will
Nancy.
N.
p cresc.
ff
Ach! Ach! kann der
Ah! Ah! Ah, will
L.
cresc.
ff
Dank, die es voll - bracht! Ach! mag der
cru - el hands were giv'n! Ah! Ah, may
Tristram.
T.
p cresc.
ff
Ach! Ach! hat sich
Ah! Ah! Can it
Plunkett.
P.
p cresc.
ff
Ach! Ach! kann der
Ah! Ah! Ah, can
ff
Knech-tes Ü - ber - muth. Was nur
turb - er of our joy. Thou shalt
Knech-tes Ü - ber - muth. Was nur
turb - er of our joy. Thou shalt
Knech-tes Ü - ber - muth. Was nur
turb - er of our joy. Thou shalt
cresc.
ff Tutti

H.
Him - mel mir ver-ge - ben, was ich that im Ü - ber-
Heav'n in-deed for-give me, That his hope I could de-
N.
Him - mel ihr ver-ge - ben, was sie that im Ü - ber-
Heav'n in-deed for-give her, That his hope she could de-
L.
Him - mel Euch ver-ge - ben, was Ihr an mir Ar - men
Heav'n a-bove for-give thee, That my life thou couldst de-
T.
end - lich ihr er-ge - ben, wie sich straft der Ü - ber-
be that she de-ceiv'd him? Do they feign their deep an-
P.
Him - mel ihr ver-ge - ben, was sie that im Ü - ber-
Heav'n in-deed for-give her, That his hopes she could de-
hat sich hier be-ge - ben? Straft des Knechtes Ü - ber-
find we'll not re-prieve thee, Hence, disturb-er of our
hat sich hier be-ge - ben? Straft des Knechtes Ü - ber-
find we'll not re-prieve thee, Hence, disturb-er of our
hat sich hier be-ge - ben? Straft des Knechtes Ü - ber-
find we'll not re-prieve thee, Hence, disturb-er of our

H.
muth? Ich ver - nich - te - te ein Le - ben,
stroy? Could he guess how it doth grieve me,
N.
muth? Sie ver - nich - te - te ein Le - ben,
stroy? But the cru - el words must grieve her,
L.
thut! Eu - er Spiel zerstört mein Le - ben,
stroy! 'Twas thy plea - sure to de - ceive me,
T.
muth? Ih - ren Ruf so preis - zu - ge - ben,
noy? It is clear that she has griev'd him,
P.
muth? Sie ver - nich - te - te ein Le - ben,
stroy? I'll be firm, I'll not re - prieve her,
muth, der mit sinn - los fre - chem Stre - ben
joy, Thou shalt find we'll not re - prieve thee,
muth, der mit sinn - los fre - chem Stre - ben
joy, Thou shalt find we'll not re - prieve thee,
muth, der mit sinn - los fre - chem Stre - ben
joy, Thou shalt find we'll not re - prieve thee,
8

poco riten. e marc.
H.
mir_ ge - weiht in treu - er Gluth.
That_ his sor - row might - al - loy.
N.
ihr_ ge - weiht in treu - er Gluth.
Love_ is che - querd with an - noy.
L.
brach mein Herz_ im Ü - ber - muth. To - des-
With_ my break - ing heart to toy. Mor - tal
T.
ha,_kaum zähm' ich mei - ne Wuth.
But_ his hopes she must de - stroy.
P.
ihr_ ge - weiht in treu - er Gluth.
For_ she's blight - ed all my joy.
stört das Fest_ in blin - der Wuth.
Hence, dis - turb - er of our joy,
stört das Fest_ in blin - der Wuth. Ja, des Knech - tes Ü - ber-
Hence, dis - turb - er of our joy, hence, dis - turb - er of our
stört das Fest_ in blin - der Wuth. Ja, des Knech - tes Ü - ber-
Hence, dis - turb - er of our joy, hence, dis - turb - er of our
poco riten. e marc.
Str.
L.
H.
Lady H.
schmerz hat mich ge - trof - fen. To - des-
pangs my bo - som rend - ing. Mor - tal
muth stört das Fest_ in blin - der Wuth!_
joy, hence, dis - turb - er of our joy._
muth stört das Fest_ in blin - der Wuth!_
joy, hence, dis - turb - er of our joy._
cresc.

p
H.
schmerz hat ihn ge - trof - fen, we - he mir, die es voll-
pangs his bo - som rend - ing, by my cru - el hands, by
Nancy.
N.
p
Kann der Him - mel ihr ver -
Ah, will Heav'n in - deed for -
Tristram.
T.
p
Ih - - ren Ruf so preis - - zu -
It is clear that she has
Plunkett.
P.
p
Kann der Him - mel ihr ver -
Ah, can Heav'n in - deed for -
H.
bracht, we - he mir!
my hands were giv'n!
N.
ge - - ben,
give her,
Lionel.
L.
Ach, mag der Him - mel Euch ver - ge - ben,
Ah, may great Heav'n a - bove for - give thee,
T.
ge - - ben,
griev'd him,
P.
ge - - ben,
give her,
Hns. & Bssn.

cresc.
H.
was ich that im Ü - ber-
that his sor-row, that his
N.
was sie that im Ü - bermuth, im Ü - ber-muth, sie that im Ü - ber-
that his hope she could destroy? His cru - el words must grieve her, love is
L.
was Ihr an mir Ar - men thut, was Ihr an mir Ar - men
that my life thou couldst de - stroy, that my life that couldst de -
T.
ihren Ruf so preis - zu - ge - ben, ha, kaum zähm' ich mei - ne
it is clear that she has griev'd him, but his hopes she must de -
P.
was sie that im Ü - bermuth, im Ü - ber-muth, ja was sie that im
that his hopes she could destroy? can Heav'n in-deed for - give her, that his
str.
cresc.
ff
poco rit.
muth, im Ü - ber - muth?
sor - row might al - loy,
muth, im Ü - ber - muth?
che - quer'd with an - noy,
thut, was Ihr an mir Ar - men thut, an mir
stroy, that my life thou couldst de - stroy, ah, thou
Wuth, kaum zähm' ich mei - ne Wuth,
stroy, ah yes, she must de - stroy,
Ü - ber - muth, im Ü - ber - muth?
hopes, his hopes she could de - stroy?
Chorus.
Stört das Fest in blin - der Wuth,
Hence, dis - turb - er of our joy,
Stört das Fest in blin - der Wuth,
Hence, dis - turb - er of our joy,
Tutti
poco rit.

H.
N.
L.
T.
P.
pp
ff
we - he mir!
ah, a - las!
we - he ihr!
with an - noy!
Ar - men thut!
couldst de - stroy!
mei - ne Wuth!
must de - stroy!
we - he ihr!
could de - stroy!
we - he ihm!
of our joy!
we - he ihm!
of our joy!
we - he ihm!
of our joy!
Allegro non troppo.
Es tönt der Ruf zur Kö - ni - gin!
The horns re - sound, the Queen is nigh!
Es tönt der Ruf zur Kö - ni - gin!
The horns re - sound, the Queen is nigh!
Es tönt der Ruf zur Kö - ni - gin!
The horns re - sound, the Queen is nigh!
Allegro non troppo.
f Hns. (on the stage)

Lionel (seized with a sudden thought).
(to Plunkett)
L.
Zur Kö - ni - gin, zur Kö - ni - gin! Nimm den Ring, sie wird mich
The Queen is nigh, the Queen is nigh! Take this ring, it will pro -
p Str.
wah - ren, wie der Va - ter einst ver - sprach, wird mich schüt - zen vor Ge -
tect me, In my fa - ther's hon - or'd name; None but these will dare sus -
(Guards separate him from Plunkett, Hunters enter with their trains.)
fah - ren, mich er - ret - ten aus der Schmach.
pect me; Go and save me fur - ther shame.
cresc.
ff Hns. (on the stage)
Chorus of Hunters and Huntresses.
Keck und mun - ter, flink hin - un - ter, fort in das Thal, fol - get dem Schall.
Bu - gles sound - ing, Gai - ly bound - ing, Fol - low the scent, fol - low the hunt,
Keck und mun - ter, flink hin - un - ter, fort in das Thal, fol - get dem Schall.
Bu - gles sound - ing, Gai - ly bound - ing, Fol - low the scent, fol - low the hunt,
Keck und mun - ter, flink hin - un - ter, fort in das Thal, fol - get dem Schall.
Bu - gles sound - ing, Gai - ly bound - ing, Fol - low the scent, fol - low the hunt,

Hört, ihr Schaa-ren, die Fan-fa-ren, fröh-lich er-schallt Waid-ruf im Wald.
We de-light-ed, They af-frigh-ted, Fol-low the horn, Fol-low till morn.
Hört, ihr Schaa-ren, die Fan-fa-ren, fröh-lich er-schallt Waid-ruf im Wald.
We de-light-ed, They af-frigh-ted, Fol-low the horn, Fol-low till morn.
Hört, ihr Schaa-ren, die Fan-fa-ren, fröh-lich er-schallt Waid-ruf im Wald.
We de-light-ed, They af-frigh-ted, Fol-low the horn, Fol-low till morn.
Tutti
Keck und mun-ter flink hin-un-ter, fort in das Thal, fol-get dem Schall,
Bu-gles sound-ing, Gai-ly bound-ing, Fol-low the scent, fol-low the hunt,
Keck und mun-ter flink hin-un-ter, fort in das Thal, fol-get dem Schall,
Bu-gles sound-ing, Gai-ly bound-ing, Fol-low the scent, fol-low the hunt,
Keck und mun-ter flink hin-un-ter, fort in das Thal, fol-get dem Schall,
Bu-gles sound-ing, Gai-ly bound-ing, Fol-low the scent, fol-low the hunt,
Full Orch.
hört, ihr Schaa-ren, die Fan-fa-ren, fröh-lich er-schallt Waid-ruf im Wald,
We de-light-ed, they af-fright-ed, Fol-low the horn, fol-low till morn.
hört, ihr Schaa-ren, die Fan-fa-ren, fröh-lich er-schallt Waid-ruf im Wald,
We de-light-ed, they af-fright-ed, Fol-low the horn, fol-low till morn.
hört, ihr Schaa-ren, die Fan-fa-ren, fröh-lich er-schallt Waid-ruf im Wald,
We de-light-ed, they af-fright-ed, Fol-low the horn, fol-low till morn.

Lady H.
H.
Weh dem Armen, kein Erbarmen,
All is o'er, in endless sorrow
Nancy.
N.
Weh dem Armen, kein Erbarmen,
All is over, endless sorrow
L.
Lionel.
Weh mir Armen, kein Erbarmen,
All is o'er, in endless sorrow
T.
Tristram.
Weh dem Armen, kein Erbarmen,
All is over, endless sorrow
folgt den Spuren auf den Fluren, hin durch Felder, in die Wälder,
Quick away, upon their traces, In all sylvan silent places,
folgt den Spuren auf den Fluren, hin durch Felder, in die Wälder,
Quick away, upon their traces, In all sylvan silent places,
p Str. & Wind.
Schmach und Grauen muss ich schauen!
I must wake each weary morrow,
Schmach und Grauen muss er schauen!
Waits on her each weary morrow,
Schmach und Grauen muss ich schauen!
I must wake each weary morrow,
Schmach und Grauen muss er schauen!
Waits on her each weary morrow,
aus den Büschen, aus den Hecken lasst das bange Reh uns schrecken,
O'er the ferny brakes and hollows Hunter bold the wild deer follows,
aus den Büschen, aus den Hecken lasst das bange Reh uns schrecken,
O'er the ferny brakes and hollows Hunter bold the wild deer follows,

H.
Weh dem Ar - men!
Ah, what sor - row!
N.
Weh dem Ar - men!
Ah, what sor - row!
L.
Weh mir Ar - men!
Ah, what sor - row!
T.
Weh dem Ar - men!
Ah, what sor - row!
un - er - mü - det, un - ver - zagt, fei - ert uns - rer Für - stin Jagd,
Till the mer - ry morn - ing break, Fol - low in the hunt - er's wake,
un - er - mü - det, un - ver - zagt, fei - ert uns - rer Für - stin Jagd,
Till the mer - ry morn - ing break, Fol - low in the hunt - er's wake,
Wind
Wind
'Cello
H.
Weh dem Ar - men!
Ah, what sor - row!
N.
Weh dem Ar - men!
Ah, what sor - row!
L.
Weh mir, weh!
Ah, what sor - row!
T.
Weh dem Ar - men!
Ah, what sor - row!
un - er - mü - det, un - ver - zagt, fei - ert der Für - stin Jagd! Tra la, tra
till the mer - ry morn - ing break, in the bold hunt - er's wake! Tra la, tra
un - er - mü - det, un - ver - zagt, fei - ert der Für - stin Jagd! Tra la, tra
till the mer - ry morn - ing break, in the bold hunt - er's wake! Tra la, tra
Hns.

la, tra la la la la, tra la, tra la, tra la la la la, tra la, tra
la, tra la la la la, tra la, tra la, tra la la la la, tra la, tra
la, tra la la la la, tra la, tra la, tra la la la la, tra la, tra
la, tra la la la la, tra la, tra la, tra la la la la, tra la, tra
la, tra la la la la, tra la, tra la, tra la la la la, tra la, tra
la, tra la la la la, tra la, tra la, tra la la la la, tra la, tra
Tutti
Hns.
Tutti
la, tra la, tra la la!
la, tra la, tra la la!
(Lionel is dragged off. Lady H. enters a litter which has been brought for her.)
la, tra la, tra la la!
la, tra la, tra la la!
(Plunkett remains holding up the ring. The train of Hunters slowly disperses.)
la, tra la, tra la la!
la, tra la, tra la la!
tr
3
ff

End of Act III.

Act IV.

The dwelling of the Farmers, as in Act II.

Nº 18. Entr'acte and Aria. „Den Theuren zu versöhnen."

Flute, Piccolo, Oboes, Clarinets in B flat, Bassoons, Horns in F & B flat, Trumpets in B flat, Trombones, Ophicleide, Kettle-drums in B flat & E flat, Big Drum, Strings, & Harp.

Recit. Lady H.
H.
Zum treu-en Freun-de geh', den Plan ihm zu ent-
Go, seek his trust-y friend, and tell him my in-
Recit.
p Str.
de-cken, den mein be-reu-end Herz voll Zu-ver-sicht er-dacht, aus dumpfer Schwermuth
ten-tion, for my re-pen-tant heart would have the tri-al o'er. To wake his dor-mant
Traum den Theu-ren zu er-we-cken mit neu-em Hoff-nungs-strahl, nach trü-ber Ker-ker-
sense, and kin-dle new with-in him the gen-tle flame of hope; to end his sor-rows
(Exit Nancy L.H.)
Andante.
nacht. Noch ver-nahm er nicht die-Kun-de, wie die Zu-kunft schön ihm
night. Still by doubt and fear-dis-tract-ed, Life for him a-gain shall
Hns.
Str.
poco animato
cresc.
tagt. Ja! Ich hei-le selbst die Wun-de, die ich schlug! Es sei ge-
smile. Ah! his sor-row, long pro-tract-ed, Now shall end, and end thro'
poco animato
Wind sustain
cresc.

H.
wagt, ja, ja, es sei ge-wagt!
me, yea, it shall end thro' me!
f
ff Tutti
ff
Moderato.
Den Theu-ren zu ver-söh-nen durch wah-re Reu', durch
I'll rouse him from his an-guish, With ten-der care, with
pp Hns. Bssn. & Hp.
wah-re Reu', sein Da-sein zu ver-schö-nen mit Lieb' und Treu', mit
ten-der care, No more his heart shall lan-guish In lone des-pair! in
f
p
ritard.
Lieb' und Treu', mein Loos mit ihm zu thei-len, durch's Le-ben hin zu
lone des-pair; With him thro' life u-nit-ed, His hopes shall be re-
colla voce
Harp & Str. pizz.
ritard.
ei-len, ach, welch
quit-ed, ah, what
colla voce

H.
Glück!
joy!
Ach! den
Ah! I'll
f Tutti
Theu-ren zu ver-söh-nen durch wah-re Reu', durch wah-re Reu', sein Da-sein zu ver-
rouse him from his an-guish With ten-der care, with ten-der care, No more his heart shall
p Wind & Harp.
ritard.
schö-nen mit Lieb' und Treu', mit Lieb' und Treu'.
lan-guish In lone des-pair, in lone des-pair.
a tempo
colla voce
ff
Tutti
Meno mosso
dolce
Ja, nun
Now at
p Str.
Hns. & Cl. sustain
darf ich frei ihm sa-gen, wie mein Herz, seit ich ihn sah, nur für
last my lips may tell him That my heart was ev-er his, Now no

H.
ihn, für ihn — ge-schlagen, ja! wie sein Bild — mir im-mer nah?
more I need — re-pel him, ah, Now my heart — may tell its bliss.
f Tutti
Ah! — O se - li - ger Ge -
Ah! — oh sweet, oh joy - ous
p Wind & Harp
dan - ke, o Hoff-nungs-schein, o Hoff-nungs-schein! Es sank die Tren-nungs -
meet - ing, Oh ray di - vine! oh ray di - vine! My heart shall give him
Poco animato.
schran-ke, mein wird er, mein, ja, mein!
greet - ing. He may, he may be mine!
ff Tutti
Ah, — ah, —
Ah, — ah, —
p Str.
Cl.

H.
ah,
ah,
ff Tutti
p Str.
H.
ja, mein wird er, mein,
ah, he may be mine,
Tutti
f
p cresc.
H.
mein wird er, mein,
oh joy, he may
H.
ja mein!
be mine!
f
ff

Nº 19. Recit. and Duet. „Willst Du mich täuschen?“

N.
trübt und still zum Bo-den nie-der, und spricht und hört kein Wort, dem kehrt das Heil nicht
sad, looks va-cant-ly be-fore him, he nei-ther speaks nor hears; I fear all change is
Lady H.
H.
O geht! Lasst mich al-lein! Ich ruf' ihn lei-se, lei-se, mit wohl-be-kann-tem
Ah, leave me here a-lone; let me but soft-ly call him, some ten-der lay may
N.
wie-der!
hope-less!
(Nancy and Plunkett retire R.H.)
H.
Lied, mit lo-ckend trau-ter Wei-se.
move, some an-cient dit-ty charm him.
Hns. & Bssn.

Tempo I.
Duet. Lady H.
H.
Ob.
p
Harp
pp Str. con sord.
Der Lenz ist ge - kom-men, die Ro - sen er - blüh'n, es strah-let die Zu-kunft im freund-li-chen Grün, es flat - tern die Blät-ter in hei - te-rer, hei - te-rer Luft, den Mat-ten er - la-bet bal - sa - mi scher Duft, den Mat-ten er - la-bet bal - sa - mi-scher Duft.
Soft breez-es are stray-ing, The ros - es ap - pear, 'Tis time for our may-ing, The heav-ens shine clear; The fu - ture is smil-ing, And sor - row shall be no more, The fair, ver - dant mead-ow has sweet flow-'ry store, the fair, ver - dant mead-ow has sweet flow-'ry store.
rit.
pp Str. trem.
(Lionel has slowly entered L.H. during the last words.)
cresc.
Tutti

Lionel.
Lady H. (hastening towards him.)
Lionel. (warding her off).
Moderato.
L.
H.
Ha! Sie! Sie ist's! Ly-o-nel! Willst Du mich täu-schen, gau-keln-des
Ha! Is it she? Li-o-nel! You would de-ceive me! You faithless
p Str.
Bild, fal-sche Sy-re-ne, mit lo-cken-dem Ko-sen? Sieh', wie Dein
mask, false as the Si-rens, you're sent to be-guile me, see how your
(takes Martha's flowers from his bosom and scatters the leaves)
glei-ssen-des Lied sich er-füllt! Sieh', wie sie flat-tern, die duf-ten-den
treacher-ous song is ful-fill'd, your flow'rs are scat-ter'd! No more you en-
Hns. & Bssn. sustain
Più animato
Lady H.
Lionel.
Ro-sen! Ly-o-nel! hör' mich! Ich kenn' dein Wort, weiss, wie es
toil me! Li-o-nel! oh hear! I know that voice, I know its
Str. & Wood
fes-selt mit ei-ser-nen Ban-den, weiss, wie es zieht zum Ver-der-ben
ma-gi-cal pow'r to en-slave me, and that des-truc-tion lurks in its
f

L.
H.
Lady H.
fort, bis dem Ver-lock-ten die Sin-ne schwan-den. Ha-be Er-
sound! Ah, go thou hence from my sight, I spurn thee. Ah no, have
Lionel.
bar-men! Er-bar-men gleich Dir, die mich ge-
mer-cy! Have mer-cy like thine? who gave me
f Tutti
f Str.
Lady H.
più lento
op-fert dem Hohn, der Schande? Sieh' mich be-reu-end, be-reu-end, zur
o-ver to pub-lic scorning? But I re-pent, I re-pent that I
p
Süh-ne hier wie ich ge-löst Dei-ne schmachvol-len Ban-de! Ich, ich
wrong'd thee so, and I my-self now will make thee a-tone-ment; I my-
più mosso
sel-ber brach-te das Pfand, das Dein Va-ter Dir ster-bend ver-
self went forth with the pledge that thy fa-ther bequeath'd thee in

H.
lieh'n, brach-te den Ring, den des Freun-des Hand Du ver-
death; I took the ring from thy trust-y friend to our
f
p
H.
trau - test, zur Herr-sche-rin. Ly-o - nel! Hör' mich! Dein ed - ler
sov - 'reign, and all is known. Li-o - nel! 'tis known thy no-ble
f Tutti
pp Str.
Recit.
Lionel.
Lady H. (giving him a parchment).
H.
L.
Va - ter war Graf Der - by, der schuldlos Ver-bann-te. O mein Va-ter! Der Kö - ni-gin
fa - ther was the great Earl of Der - by, long banish'd. Oh my fa-ther! The Queen, ev-er
Recit.
a tempo
H.
Gna - de lohnt es dem Soh - ne jetzt huldreich und mild. Graf von Der - by! Auf ruhm-vol-lem
gracious, glad-ly re-calls what un-just-ly was done. Earl of Der - by, in hon-or and
Brass
marziale
Lionel.
H.
L.
Pfa - de tragt Eu-rer Ah - nen glor-rei-ches Schild. Ich! Graf Der - by. Ich! Graf
glo - ry, own thy an - ces - tral ti - tle and lands. I a Der - by! Earl of
f Tutti
Vl.
p
Str.

Lady H.
L.
H.
Der - by! Und die - se Hand, die Dir rei - chet der Zu-kunft Se - gen,
Der - by? And take this hand, if thou wilt, in thine own for ev - er,
pp
più animato
beut sich der Dei - nen als Un-ter-pfand mei - ner Reu - e, mei - ner
thine in a ten - der and last-ing band, thine for ev - er, ne'er to
più animato
Lionel.
Lie - be, mei - ner Reu', mei - ner Lie - be ent - ge - gen. Die - se
sev - er; I have wrong'd thee, and now sue for par - don. What, thy
Lady H.
In Lieb' und Reu - e, in Lieb' und Reu - e, in Lieb' und
I know I wrong'd thee, and sue thy par - don, I sue thy
Lionel.
Hand?
hand?
Str. & Wind
cresc.
Reu - e.
par - don!
ff Tutti

Andante con moto.
Lionel.
L.
Die - se Hand, die sich ge-wen-det, um mich schmachvoll fort-zu -
With this hand up-rais'd in scorn-ing from your pre-sence you ex -
p
Str. pizz. Hns. & Bssn. sustain
wei-sen, die-se Hand, die mir ge-sen-det har-ter Ban-de kal-tes
pell'd me, from this hand this ve-ry morn-ing came the bonds that base - ly
Ei-sen, die bald win-ket, bald ver-scheu-chet, und mit schnö - dem Netz um-
bound me; now it beck-ons, then it threat-ens, where's the pro - mise you have
poco più animato
Cello
(throws the parchment at her feet)
con forza
flicht, die-se Hand, die mir sich rei - chet, die-se Hand! ich will sie
kept? 'Tis a hand of guile and false - ness, and this hand I'll not ac -
Wind sustain
cresc.
Tutti
ff
Andante.
Lady H.
L.
H.
nicht! Gros-ser Gott!
cept! Gracious Heav'n!
Lionel.
O! We-he mir!
Oh bit-ter grief!
pp Harp, Hns. & Bssn. sustain.

L.
Sie war mein Stern, mein höch-stes Gut! Ihr weiht' ich
She was my hope, my on-ly joy! For her sweet
cresc.
L.
gern mein treu-es Blut! Sie war mein Glück! Zu Him-mels-
sake I'd glad-ly die! She was my all, oh bit-ter
L.
H.
poco animato
Lady H.
lust durchdrang ihr Blick die hoch-be-seel-te Brust. Sieh' mei-nen
smart! Her ra-diant glance with rap-ture fir'd my heart. Oh let thy
f
colla voce
pp
Str. trem.
H.
Schmerz, sieh' mei-ne Reu', es schlägt mein Herz Dir wahr und
gen-tle heart re-lent, For-give thy wrongs, as I re-
Harp
H.
treu. Ge-wiss es kehrt das Heil zu-rück, und neu ver-
pent, Ah, hap-py days can e'er re-turn, The flame of
L.
Nein! Nim-mer kehrt das Heil zu-rück, da-hin, zer-
No hap-py days can e'er re-turn, Of ev-'ry
pp
Harp

H.
klärt sich un - ser Glück, ja, neu ver - klärt sich un - ser Glück.
joy a - gain shall burn, the flame of joy a - gain shall burn.
L.
stört ist all' mein Glück, ja, zer - stört ist all' mein Glück, ist all' mein
joy my life is shorn, yes, a - las, of ev - 'ry joy my life is
colla voce
Cl.
H.
Sieh' mei - nen Schmerz, sieh' mei - ne Reu', es schlägt mein
Oh let thy gen - tle heart re - lent, for - give thy
L.
Glück! Nein! nim - mer kehrt mein Heil zu - rück, da - hin, zer -
shorn! No hap - py days can e'er re - turn, of ev - 'ry
Str. trem.
Wind sustain
cresc.
H.
f
ad lib.
Herz Dir wahr und treu, gewiss, es kehrt das Heil zu - rück, und neu verklärt sich un - ser, un - ser
wrongs as I re - pent, ah hap - py days, will yet re - turn, the flame of joy a - gain, a - gain shall
L.
f
ad lib.
stört ist all' mein Glück, nein, nimmer kehrt mein Heil zu - rück, da - hin, zer - stört ist all' mein
joy my life is shorn, of ev - 'ry joy my life is shorn, of ev - 'ry joy my life is
f
ff
colla voce
Allegro vivace.
H.
Glück. Ja! Es kehrt das Heil zu - rück,
burn. Hap - py days will yet re - turn,
L.
Glück, ach! zer - stört ist all' mein Glück,
shorn. Ah, of joy my life is shorn,
Tutti

H.
das Heil zu - rück, ja, es
will yet re - turn, hap - py
L.
ist all' mein Glück, ja, zer -
my life is shorn, ah, of
H.
kehrt das Heil zu - rück ja, es kehrt das Heil zu - rück!
days will yet re - turn, hap - py days will yet re - turn!
L.
stört ist all' mein Glück. Fort! Hin-weg, ich has - se Dich,
joy my life is shorn! Maid - en false, I'll hear no more,
H.
Ly - o - nel, er - bar - me Dich, Ly - o - nel, Du töd-test mich, Du töd - test mich!
Li - o - nel, oh hear my pray'r, Li o nel, Li - o - nel, thou wilt break my heart!
L.
fal-sches Weib, ich has - se Dich, fal-sches Weib, ich has-se Dich, ich has - se Dich!
maid - en false, I'll hear no more, maid - en false, ah, no more! from thee I must part!
ff
(Lionel rushes off L. H. Lady Harriet sinks on a couch.)

Nº 20. Recitative. „Fasst Euch, Lady!"

Allegro con moto.
'Cello, Bass pizz. & Bssn.
Vl. & Cl.
Plunkett.
Ja, was nun?
What's to do?
Str. & Wind
Ob. & Bssn.
Nancy.
Ja, was nun? Was nun thun?
What's to do? And un - do?
Plunkett.
Ja, was nun thun?
What is to do?
Str. pizz.
Wind
Str.
Hn.
Nancy.
Schnell der La - dy Wunsch er - fül - len, treu voll - füh - ren ih - ren
We must now show our al - legiance By a true and full o -
Vl. arco & Cl.
Wil - len, bis der stol - ze Herr ge - neigt sich her - ab zu las - sen
be - dience To her way - ward plan and mood, Till her proud swain is sub -
Ob. Cl. & Hns.
Str.
zeigt.
dued.
Wind
Plunkett.
A - ber dann?
Well, what then?
Nancy.
Ja, was
Ah, what

Plunkett.
Nancy.
Plunkett.
N.
P.
dann? Wann's ge - than, was dann? Was dann? Ach, dann sitz' ich ganz al -
then? When that's done, what then? What then? I shall then be left quite
add Str. pizz.
lei - ne, ganz al - lei - ne, ganz al - lei - ne, A - bends bei des Lämpchens
lone - ly, left quite lone - ly, sad and lone - ly, Of one dam - sel think - ing
Cl.
p Str. arco
Scheine, ein - sam hier, im ö - den Haus_ Ei! das halt ein And'rer aus. Ja, dann sitzt Ihr ganz al -
on - ly, Whom to court I do not dare; No, it's more than I can bear! Ah, in - deed, will you be
f Str. Wind
lei - ne, ja, dann sitzt Ihr ganz al - lei - ne, A - bends
lone - ly? Ah, in - deed, will you be lone - ly? Think - ing
Ja, dann sitz' ich ganz al - lei - ne, ganz al - lei - ne, ganz al -
Yes, in - deed I shall be lone - ly, yes, in - deed I shall be
Fl. & Ob.
bei dem Lämp - chen, ein - sam hier im ö - den Haus.
of one dam - sel, whom to court you do not dare?
lei - ne, A - bends bei des Lämpchens Scheine, ein - sam hier im ö - den Haus. Nein!
lone - ly, Think - ing of one dam - sel on - ly, Whom to court I do not dare, No!
f

N.
P.
Nein! Das hal - tet Ihr nicht aus. Trüb' ist das!
Ah! is't more than you can bear? That is sad!
nein, das halt ein And'rer aus.
it is more than I can bear.
p Wind
Str.
Wind
Wisst Ihr was? Gelt! Ihr
I've a thought! Why, of
Ja, kein Spass! Nun was? ja, was?
'Tis too bad! Well, speak it out.
Wind
Str.
müsst ein Weibchen wäh-len, seid ja alt ge - nug und reich!
course, you ought to mar - ry, That will all your cares dis - pel.
Na! Das
Ah, for
Wind
So? Das scheint ihn nicht zu
Mighty fine! then do not
soll - te mich nicht quä-len, Nachbars Pol-ly nimmt mich gleich, Nach - bars
that I need not tar - ry, Farmer's Pol - ly likes me well, Farm - er's
Str.

N.
quä - len, Nach-bars Pol - ly nimmt ihn gleich, so, das scheint ihn nicht zu
tar - ry, Farm-er's Pol - ly likes you well, migh - ty fine! then do not
P.
Pol - ly nimmt mich gleich, Nach - bars
Pol - ly likes me well, Farm - er's
quä-len, Nachbars Pol-ly nimmt ihn gleich. Wohl! nur zu!
tar-ry, Farmer's Pol-ly likes you well. Mar-ry her!
Pol - ly nimmt mich gleich. Lasst mich in
Pol - ly likes me well. Let me a -
f Str. & Wind
Doch wa-rum? Müsst denn ei - ne An - dre
Pray sir, why? In that case, quick, choose an -
Ruh'! Sie ist so dumm!
lone! A stu - pid wench!
p Str.
wäh-len, ob's an Mäd-chen wohl ge - bricht?
oth - er, maids for ask - ing may be had.
Rich-ters Ann' würd' sich be -
Sher - iff's Anne per - haps would
Wind

N.
P.
Rich-ters Ann' würd'sich be -
Sher-iff's Anne per-haps would
que - men, a - ber nein, die mag ich nicht! Rich - ters
have me, But her tem-per'd drive me mad, Yes, her
Str.
que-men, a-ber nein, die mag er nicht, Rich-ters Ann' würd' sich be -
have you? pit - y that her tem-per's bad! Sher-iff's Anne per - haps would
Ann', die mag ich nicht, nein, nein,
tem - per'd drive me mad, no, no,
quemen, a-ber nein, die mag er nicht! Suchet denn
have you? pit-y that her temper's bad! You must search
nein, die mag ich nicht! Ja wo? Ja
no, she will not do. But where? but
f
Weiss denn ich's?
I don't know.
ritard.
wo? Ja so! Ja so! Ah so!
where? In-deed! in-deed! in-deed!
Str.
Wind
dim.
ritard.

Meno mosso.
P.
O! Ich wüss-te wohl schon Ei-ne; ist sie gleich sehr hoch hinaus, passt sie gleich, die,
Oh, I know a bon-ny las-sie, But she holds her head too high; And her tongue is
colla voce
Str. & Ob. Hn. sustain
die ich mei-ne, gar nicht für mein ein-fach Haus; kann sie gleich nicht einmal spinnen,
pert and sau-cy, And she'll in a passion fly; Thrift-y house-wife is not in her,
ist sie gleich sehr un-geschickt wusst' sie doch mich zu gewinnen, seit ich ihr in's
She can nei-ther spin nor cook; But what would I give to win her, What but for a
Nancy.
N.
Aug'geblickt! Ei! ihr ma-let, wie ich mei-ne, sie höchst schmeichelhaft mir aus;
tender look! Ah, you paint a flatt'ring picture, Fresh from life, I must admit;
zwar sie passet nicht, die Ei-ne, die Ihr meint, für Eu-er Haus; doch sie lernt wohl
But from all I can con-jecture, For your home she's scarce-ly fit; As for cook-ing
bald zu spinnen, bleibt nicht immer un-geschickt, wenn es gilt Euch zu gewin-nen,
and for spinning, These are arts can be acquir'd; If your hand she's bent on winning,

N.
wenn sie solchen Mann erblickt. Ei freilich.
Soon you'll own the boon de-sir'd. Plunkett. Well, why not?
P.
Wahr? O, dann sagt mir
True? Then, o tell me
Cl.
Fl. & Picc.
f
p
Was?
What?
Nein, sagt's noch nicht! Ly-o-nel geht
No, speak not yet! Li-o-nel comes
Ob. & Cl.
Ach!
Ah!
vor denn hei-lig ist mir treu-er Freundschaft Pflicht! Ja,
first; for sa-cred, sa-cred shall be friendship's trust! A-
ritard.
So sprecht! Ach so sprecht! Ach so
Say on! Nay, say on! Nay, say
ach! Ge-mach! Nur ge-mach!
las! There's time! Wait a-while!
Wind
Str.

Più animato.
N.
sprecht! Erst der Freundschaft Stimme hört' er,
on! Love with you gives way to friendship,
P.
Nur ge-mach! Erst der Freundschaft Stimme hör' ich,
Wait a-while! Love with me gives way to friendship,
Più animato.
Str. & Ob.
Hns. & Bssn. sustain
seinen starren Sinn beschwört' er, Und dann wagt er,
In your stubborn mood you glo - ry. Yet he woos me,
seinen starren Sinn beschwör' ich,
In my stubborn mood I glo - ry.
und dann sagt er, und dann wagt er, und dann fragt er_
yet he sues me. If he woos me, he must choose me.
und dann wag' ich, und dann sag' ich,
Yet I woo ye, and I sue ye.
Ach,
Ah,
und dann frag' ich Euch, ja, Euch ein Wort, ja, Euch ein
Las-sie, I will woo and choose ye too, and choose ye
Str.

N.
— ja, dann fra-get Er ein Wort, ja, ein Wort ja, — ah, —
— ask me just to say one word, just one word, ask, — ah, —
P.
Wort, und dann frag'ich Euch ein Wort, ja, ein Wort, ja, ein Wort, und dann
too, yes I'll ask you for one word, for one word, for one word, I will
N.
— ja, dann fra-get Er ein Wort, ja, dann
— ask me just to say one word, ask me
P.
frag' ich Euch ein Wort, ja, dann frag'ich Euch ein Wort, ja, dann
ask you for one word, I will ask you for one word, I will
Tutti
cresc.
or
ein Wort!
one word!
N.
fra - get Er ein Wort! Ja, — ein Wort!
just to say one word, ah, — one word!
P.
frag' ich Euch ein Wort! Ja, ein Wort!
ask you for one word, for one word!
f
ff
Tutti
(Exeunt through centre door.)

Nº 21. Finale. – „Hier die Buden, dort die Schenke.“

Scene changes. Outside Plunkett's farmhouse. Farmers and servants are busy placing tents, booths, benches, etc., as they were at Richmond fair. Some are dressing up a farmer like the Sheriff.

dort die Mie-ther, und der Rich-ter als Ge-bie-ter mit dem Sta-be
look for plac-es, Mas-ters here, with scan-ning fac-es, That's the Sher-iff's
dort die Mie-ther, und der Rich-ter als Ge-bie-ter mit dem Sta-be
look for plac-es, Mas-ters here, with scan-ning fac-es, That's the Sher-iff's
dort die Mie-ther, und der Rich-ter als Ge-bie-ter mit dem Sta-be
look for plac-es, Mas-ters here, with scan-ning fac-es, That's the Sher-iff's
und Ta-lar, g'ra-de wie es da-mals war. Hier die
haugh-ty air, Just as 'twas at Rich-mond fair. All's in
und Ta-lar, g'ra-de wie es da-mals war. Hier die
haugh-ty air, Just as 'twas at Rich-mond fair. All's in
und Ta-lar, g'ra-de wie es da-mals war.
haugh-ty air, Just as 'twas at Rich-mond fair.
p Str. & Wind
Bu-den, hier die Zel-te,
or-der, all's in or-der,
Bu-den, hier die Zel-te,
or-der, all's in or-der,
Dort die Schen-ke,
There's the ta-vern,

hier der Tisch
in his chair,
hier der Tisch
in his chair,
vorn die Bän - ke,
Here's the Sher - iff,
für den No-
'tis Richmond
8
g'ra - de, g'ra - de,
yes, ex - act - ly,
ja, g'ra-de
yes, 'tis ex-
g'ra - de, g'ra - de,
yes, ex - act - ly,
ja, g'ra-de
yes, 'tis ex-
tar,
fair,
wie es da-mals war, ja, g'ra-de
just like Richmond fair, yes, 'tis ex-
8
wie, ja, g'ra-de wie es da-mals war, ja, g'ra - de wie, ja, wie es
act - ly as it was at Richmond fair, ex - act - ly as it was at
wie, ja, g'ra-de wie es da-mals war, ja, g'ra - de wie, ja, wie es
act - ly as it was at Richmond fair, ex - act - ly as it was at
wie, ja, g'ra-de wie es da-mals war, ja, g'ra - de wie, ja, wie es
act - ly as it was at Richmond fair, ex - act - ly as it was at
cresc.

da-mals war. Hier die Bu-den, dort die Schen-ke, hier die Zel-te,
Rich-mond fair. Here are tents and booths in or-der, there's the ta-vern,
p leggiero
vorn die Bän-ke, hier der Tisch für den No-tar, g'ra-de wie es da-mals war.
yon's the war-der, Here's the Sher-iff's great arm-chair, Just as 'twas at Rich-mond fair.
Cl.
p
Str.
Wind
Enter Lady H. (attired as Martha).
H.
Nun, ihr Freunde! Ist's ge-sche-hen?
Friends, ye're welcome! you've o-bey'd me.

Chorus.
Nach Befehl_ Hier die Buden,
All's prepar'd_ Tents and boothshere,
Mög't selber seh'n, mög't selber sehen! dort die Schenke,
Look round and see how we've obey'd you! there's the tavern,
Mög't selber sehen! Hier die Zelte,
How we've obey'd you! Yon's the warder,
vorn die Bänke, hier der Tisch für den Notar, ja, g'rade wie es damals war, und der
yes, and here's the haughty Sheriff's great arm-chair, just as it was at Richmond fair; Here are
Wind
Str.
Str. & Wind
cresc.

Rich - ter als Ge - bie - ter mit dem Sta - be und Ta - lar, die Bu - den,
maids who look for plac - es, Mas - ters there with scanning fac - es, Tents and
Rich - ter als Ge - bie - ter mit dem Sta - be und Ta - lar, die Bu - den,
maids who look for plac - es, Mas - ters there with scanning fac - es, Tents and
Rich - ter als Ge - bie - ter mit dem Sta - be und Ta - lar, die Bu - den,
maids who look for plac - es, Mas - ters there with scanning fac - es, Tents and
f Tutti
dort die Schen - ke, hier die Zel - te, vorn - die Bän - ke, hier der Tisch für
booths in or - der, There's the ta - vern, yon's the war - der, Here's the Sher - iff's
dort die Schen - ke, hier die Zel - te, vorn die Bän - ke, hier der Tisch für
booths in or - der, There's the ta - vern, yon's the war - der, Here's the Sher - iff's
dort die Schen - ke, hier die Zel - te, vorn die Bän - ke, hier der Tisch für
booths in or - der, There's the ta - vern, yon's the war - der, Here's the Sher - iff's
den No - tar, g'ra - de wie es da - mals war, ja, g'ra - de wie es, g'ra - de wie es
great arm - chair, Just as 'twas at Rich - mond fair, just as it was, just as it was, just
den No - tar, g'ra - de wie es da - mals war, ja, g'ra - de wie es, g'ra - de wie es
great arm - chair, Just as 'twas at Rich - mond fair, just as it was, just as it was, just
den No - tar, g'ra - de wie es da - mals war, ja, g'ra - de wie es, g'ra - de wie es
great arm - chair, Just as 'twas at Rich - mond fair, just as it was, just as it was, just

da-mals war, ja, g'ra - de wie es, g'ra-de, g'ra-de wie es da-mals
as it was, just as it was, just as it was at mer-ry Richmond
da-mals war, ja, g'ra - de wie es, g'ra-de, g'ra-de wie es da-máls
as it was, just as it was, just as it was at mer-ry Richmond
da-mals war, ja, g'ra - de wie es, g'ra-de, g'ra-de wie es da-mals
as it was, just as it was, just as it was at mer-ry Richmond
cresc.
war, hier den Tisch für den No - tar, g'ra - de wie es da - mals
fair, here's the Sher-iff's great arm - chair, just as 'twas at Rich-mond
war, hier den Tisch für den No - tar, g'ra - de wie es da - mals
fair, here's the Sher-iff's great arm - chair, just as 'twas at Rich-mond
war, hier den Tisch für den No - tar, g'ra - de wie es da - mals
fair, here's the Sher-iff's great arm - chair, just as 'twas at Rich-mond
ff
war, ja, g'ra - de wie es da - mals war, ja, g'ra - de wie es da - mals
fair, just as it was at Rich-mond fair, just as it was at Rich-mond
war, ja, g'ra - de wie es da - mals war, ja, g'ra - de wie es da - mals
fair, just as it was at Rich-mond fair, just as it was at Rich-mond
war, ja, g'ra - de wie es da - mals war, ja, g'ra - de wie es da - mals
fair, just as it was at Rich-mond fair, just as it was at Rich-mond

Andante.
war.
fair.
war.
fair.
war.
fair.
Andante.
Hn.
'Cello solo
pp
Vla.'Cello & Bass
Lady H.
Ach! mir
Ah, I
Enter Nancy (as Julia).
Seht, dort naht er_ trüb' ge-leh-net auf den Freund, der ihn beglei-tet.
Ah, I see him, com - ing tow'rd us, on his friend he's leaning sad-ly.
Cl.
dolce
bangget_
tremble!
Nancy.
Der Stolze wähnet nicht,
Ah me, what will he say,
Chorus.
pp
Seht! dort naht er_ trüb' ge-leh-net auf den Freund,
Look, be-hold him, com - ing tow'rd us, on his friend
pp
Seht! dort naht er_ trüb' ge-leh-net auf den Freund,
Look, be-hold him, com - ing tow'rd us, on his friend
pp
Seht! dort naht er_ trüb' ge-leh-net auf den Freund,
Look, be-hold him, com - ing tow'rd us, on his friend
pp Str. & Hns.

Animato.
N.
wo-hin die List ihn lei - tet, wo-hin die List ihn lei - tet!
When he the truth dis - cov - ers? when he the truth dis - cov - ers?
der ihn be - glei - tet, der ihn be - glei - tet!
he's leaning sad - ly, he's lean-ing sad-ly.
Animato.
Tutti
cresc.
Allegretto.
Nancy.
Jetzt, Ihr Freun - de, Jung und Alt! der Markt be -
Come, good friends, both young and old, The fair be -
f Bssn. p Fl. Picc. & Ob.
ritard.
Allegro.
ginnt, die Glocke schallt!
gins, the bell hath toll'd!
Chorus.
SOPRANO & ALTO.
(They assume their places as in Act I.)
Ich kann nä-hen, ich kann mähen, ich kann
I can sow, sir, I can mow sir, I can
Allegro.
f Str. colla voce
f Tutti
sä-en, Fä-den dre-hen, ich kann bü-geln, ich kann striegeln und ver - se-hen Hof und
bake and brew, Mend things like new, Can mind a house and rule it too, There's naught I can not

Haus! Ja, ich kann nä-hen, ich kann mä-hen, ich kann sä-en, Fä-den
do, yes, I can sow, and I can mow, and I can bake and brew, mend
Wol-len se-hen, wie sie mä-hen, wie sie sä-en, Fä-den
Let us see then, and a-gree then how you sow and mow and
Wol-len se-hen, wie sie mä-hen, wie sie sä-en, Fä-den
Let us see then, and a-gree then how you sow and mow and
marcato
dre-hen, ich kann bü-geln, ich kann strie-geln und ver-se-hen Hof und
things like new, can mind a house and rule it too, there's naught I can-not
dre-hen, wie sie_ bü-geln, wie sie strie-geln und ver-se-hen Hof und
bake and brew, if_ on-ly half you say is true, we'll pay and thank you
dre-hen, wie sie_ bü-geln, wie sie strie-geln und ver-se-hen Hof und
bake and brew, if_ on-ly half you say is true, we'll pay and thank you
Plunkett (leading Lionel forward).
P.
Na! nur zu_ und nicht so sprö-de,
Well, come on, no need of shy-ness,
Haus, ja, ich kann nä-hen, ich kann mä-hen, ich kann sä-en, Fä-den dre-hen, ich kann
do, yes, I can sow, and I can mow, and I can bake and I can brew, and I can
Haus, ja, wol-len se-hen, wie sie mä-hen, wie sie sä-en, Fä-den dre-hen, wie sie
too, yes, let us see, and then a-gree, how you can sow and mow, and bake and brew, if
Haus, ja, wol-len se-hen, wie sie mä-hen, wie sie sä-en, Fä-den dre-hen, wie sie
too, yes, let us see, and then a-gree, how you can sow and mow, and bake and brew, if

Lionel (without perceiving Martha).
L.
P.
Ha! Was
Ah, where
mach's wie ich und sei nicht blö-de!
do like me, I'm not for coyness!
bü-geln, ich kann strie-geln und ver-se-hen Hof und Haus!
mind a house and rule it too, there's naught I can-not do!
bü-geln, wie sie strie-geln und ver-se-hen Hof und Haus!
on-ly half you say is true, we'll pay and thank you too!
bü-geln, wie sie strie-geln und ver-se-hen Hof und Haus!
on-ly half you say is true, we'll pay and thank you too!
p Str.
Plunkett.
seh' ich? Hüb-sche Kinder! Die, und Die, und
am I? 'Mongst the lass-es! Look, here's one and
(bringing forward Lady Harriet)
Die nicht minder. Sprich! Was kannst Du? sag' es frei!
there's an-other. What can you do? dam-sel, say!
f
p Wind sustain
Lionel.
Martha! Martha! Gro-sser Gott!
Martha! Martha! Gra-cious Heav'n!
cresc.
f Tutti

Andante.
Lady H.
H.
Ich kann ent - sa-gen dem Glanz, dem Schimmer, kann oh-ne Za-gen sie fliehn auf
I can, renounce rank and worldly splen - dor, A heart devot-ed I can sur-
Hns.
p
Str. Hns. sustain
immer! Ich kann dem Treu-en mein Dasein wei-hen, ich kann ihm sa-gen: nur Dir al-
ren-der, I can re - ply to a passion ten-der, Can say: I'll love thee, and thee a -
Più animato.
Lionel.
H.
L.
lein will ich, will ich mich weih'n! O Him-mels-glück, o
lone, I'll love but thee a - lone. Oh joy of Heav'n, oh
f
Tutti
Plunkett.
meno mosso
L.
P.
Him - mels - glück! Na! Du Mädel, was kannst Du?
joy of Heav'n! Well, good lassie, what can you?
p Str.
Hns.
Più lento
Nancy (roguishly).
Plunkett (threatening her).
Nancy.
N.
P.
Fei-nes Linnen kann ich spinnen. Du kannst lügen und be - trügen – Und dich
I'm for spinning fin-est lin-en. For de - ceiving and in - triguing – And to –
Str.

Plunkett.
N.
P.
schmiegen und dich bie-gen, zu er-lie-gen mei-nem Joch! Topp! Mädel,'sgilt der
gov-ern you and form you in-to all that I_ de-sire, Done! Then the bargain's
f
p
Nancy.
Plunkett.
P.
N.
Kauf! Topp! Nimm das Handgeld d'rauf! Solch ein Handgeld soll mir frommen, wart', das
made. Done! Here's the handsel paid! Naught but joy shall fol-low af-ter, Though the
Chorus.
Ha, ha, ha, ha, er hat's ge-nom-men, mag das
Ha, ha, ha, ha, the bargain's made, the mon-ey's
Ha, ha, ha, ha, er hat's ge-nom-men, mag das
Ha, ha, ha, ha, the bargain's made, the mon-ey's
Ha, ha, ha, ha, er hat's ge-nom-men, mag das
Ha, ha, ha, ha, the bargain's made, the mon-ey's
f
p
f Tutti
Andante.
Lady H. (giving her flowers to Lionel).
P.
N.
soll Dir schön be-kommen! Der_ Lenz ist ge-
bargain's made in laughter! Soft_ breez-es are_
Hand-geld ihm be-kom-men. Ha, ha, ha, ha, ha, ha, ha!
paid, 'tis paid in laughter! Ha, ha, ha, ha, ha, ha, ha!
Hand-geld ihm be-kom-men. Ha, ha, ha, ha, ha, ha, ha!
paid, 'tis paid in laughter! Ha, ha, ha, ha, ha, ha, ha!
Hand-geld ihm be-kom-men. Ha, ha, ha, ha, ha, ha, ha!
paid, 'tis paid in laughter! Ha, ha, ha, ha, ha, ha, ha!
Andante.
p Harp & Wind

Lionel.
H.
L.
kommen, die_ Ro - sen er-blü'hn. Es_strahlet die Zukunft im_ freund-lichen
stray-ing, The ros - es ap-pear. 'Tis time for our maying, The_ heav-ens shine
Lady H.
H.
Es_ flat - tern die Blät-ter in_ hei - te-rer,
The_ fu - ture is smil-ing, and_ sor - row shall
L.
Grün, es_ flat - tern die Blät-ter in_ hei - te-rer,
clear, The_ fu - ture is smil-ing, and_ sor - row shall
Lady H.
rit.
f
H.
hei - te-rer Luft, zum Hei-le, zum Glü-cke das_ Da-sein uns ruft, zum
be_ no more, Love's blessed en-chantment your hearts_shall re-store, love's
Nancy.
N.
Zum Hei-le, zum Glü-cke das_ Da-sein uns ruft, zum
Love's blessed en-chantment your hearts_shall re-store, love's
Lionel.
L.
hei - te-rer Luft, zum Hei-le, zum Glü-cke das_ Da-sein uns ruft, zum
be_ no more, Love's blessed en-chantment your hearts shall re-store, love's
Plunkett.
P.
Zum Hei-le, zum Glü-cke das_ Da-sein uns ruft, zum
Love's blessed en-chantment your hearts shall re-store, love's
Chorus.
Zum Hei-le, zum_ Glü-cke das_ Da-sein uns ruft, zum
Love's bless-ed en-chant-ment your hearts_shall re-store, love's
Zum Hei-le, zum Glü-cke das_ Da-sein uns ruft, zum
Love's bless-ed en-chant-ment your hearts shall re-store, love's
Zum Hei-le, zum Glü-cke das_ Da-sein uns ruft, zum
Love's bless-ed en-chant-ment your hearts shall re-store, love's
colla voce
ff
Tutti

End of the Opera.

Appendix

No. 14. Nancy's Aria

A supplementary aria, written for Mme. Nantier-Didiée

"Esser mesto il mio cor non sapria,,
„Nimmermehr wird mein Herze sich grämen"

English and German versions by Dr. Th. Baker

spi - ro non so co - sa si - a, so-spi-rar a vent' an - ni,e per-chè? Pu-re io
nicht, was ein Seufzer be - deu -tet, bin so jung noch, wo - zu Weh' und Ach? Doch ich
ne'er_ spent a mo-ment in sigh-ing, And at twen-ty for what should one sigh? Yet I
sen - to u-na vo - ce nel cor;_ che vuoi dal cor; vo - ce d'a-
hör'_ ei - ne Stim-me im Her-zen: Was kann das sein? Lie-be al-
hear_ how a voice in my heart_ Whis-pers of love: what would it
mor? Ah! So - spi-rar si può d'a-mor, sì, so - spi-rar si può d'a-
lein! Ja! seuf - zen kann, wer recht ver-liebt! ja, seuf-zen kann, wer recht ver-
tell? Ah! one_ might sigh for love, in-deed! ay, one might sigh for love, in-
cresc. poco a
mor! Fe - li-ce il cuo - re che al-ber-ga a - mo - re, la vi-ta è un
liebt! Glück-lich das Herz, wo Lie - be ruft,_ sein Le-ben die
deed! Hap-py the heart where love_ may dwell,_ For life is a
cresc. poco a

poco
f
fior, lo-lez-zo è a-mor, ah! So-spi-rar si
Blu-me und Lie-be der Duft! Ja! seuf-zen kann, wer
flow'r and love is the sweet! Ay, one might sigh for
poco
f
p
può d'a-mor, so-spi-rar si può d'a-mor, so-spi-
recht ver-liebt! seuf-zen kann, werrecht ver-liebt! seuf-zen
love, in-deed, one might sigh for love, in-deed, one might
pp
rar si può d'a-mor, ah! d'a-
kann, werrecht ver-liebt! ja! ver-
sigh, in-deed, for love! ay! for
mf
mor, ah! d'a-mor!
liebt! ach! ver-liebt!
love! ah! for love!
pp

So - spi - rar si può d'a - mor! ___
Seuf - zen kann, wer recht ver - liebt! ___
One might sigh, in - deed, for love! ___
Allegro
f
The Huntresses return
ritenuto
Allegro non troppo
Nancy
Il tuo stral nel lan-ciar, gio-vin cac-cia - tri - ce,
Jä - ge-rin, schlau im Sinn, zie-let mit den Bli - cken,
With her eye, ev - er sly, See the hunt-ress aim - ing,
p

non tar-dar, non tre-mar, ti - tu-bar non li - ce, dei col-pir, dei fe-rir
weiss in Eil' Pfeil auf Pfeil aus dem Aug' zu schi-cken; oh - ne Ruh' im-mer-zu
At the heart man-ya dart Send her glanc-es flam-ing. Day by day for the prey
la bel-va ed il co - re, tri - on-far, pre - da far di cac-cia e da-
wacht sie un-ver - dros - sen, lau - ert schlau, zielt ge-nau, bis das Wild ge-
Pa-tient - ly she watch - es, Wide a-wake aim to take Till her game she
mo - - - - - - - re. È l'A-mor un cac - cia - tor,
schos - - - - - - - sen! A - mor, das ver - schmitz-te Kind,
catch - - - - - - - es! Cu - pid, with his ro - guish art,
il suo stral sa lan-ciar; ma se im-pia-ga, sa quel duol al - leg -
trug den Pfeil wie der Wind, A - mor trug den Pfeil ge - schwind wie der
Like the wind bore the dart, Cu - pid, with his ro - guish art, bore the
f

giar! È l'A-mor un cac - cia - tor, il suo stral
Wind! A - mor, das ver-schmitz-te Kind, trug den Pfeil
dart! Cu - pid, with his ro - guish art, Like the wind
Chorus of Huntresses
Sì, è l'A - mor un cac - cia - to - re, il suo stra - le sa lan -
Ja, A - mor, das ver-schmitz - te Kind, es trug den Pfeil ge-schwind ge -
Yes, Cu-pid, with his ro - guish art, now like the wind he bore the
sa lan-ciar; ma se im-pia - ga, sa quel duol al - leg - giar!
wie der Wind, A - mor trug den Pfeil ge - schwind wie der Wind!
bore the dart, Cu - pid with his art, his art, bore the dart!
cia - re; ma se im-pia-ga, sa quel duol, ah! al - leg-giar!
schwind, ja, A - mor trug den Pfeil ge-schwind, ge - schwind wie der Wind!
dart, ay, Cu-pid, with his ro-guish art, ah! bore the dart!

Nancy
Sì, la pre - da che vo - gliam, con lar-mi non pren - diam, vi-va es-sa dee ca-der-ci al piè, sì, ne siam noi che - la cer - chiam, spes-so fug-gir, fug - gir dob-biam, ma nel fug - gir sap-piam, sap - piam fe - rir, ah! fe-rir sap - piam!
Doch die Beu - te, so man hält, mit Waf-fen nimmt man nicht, zu Fü-ssen uns sie le - bend fällt! Nein, auf die Jagd sind wir nie er - picht, gar oft man flie-hen, flie-hen soll! je-doch im Flie-hen trifft, ja, trifft man wohl, ja! trifft man wohl!
Ay, what-e'er the game we meet, We do not shoot to kill; It falls a-live be-fore our feet! No! chase the game we nev-er, nev-er will, In-deed, we of-ten flee a-way, Yet, tho' in flight, we wound, we wound our prey, ah! we wound our prey!
f

più facile
È l'A-mor un cac-cia-tor, il suo stral sa lan-ciar;
A-mor, das verschmitz-te Kind, trug den Pfeil wie der Wind,
Cu-pid, with his ro-guish art, Like the wind bore the dart!
ma se im-pia-ga, sa quel duol al-leg-giar; è l'A-mor un
A-mor trug den Pfeil ge-schwind wie der Wind! A-mor, das ver-
Cu-pid, with his ro-guish art, bore the dart! Cu-pid, with his
Chorus of Huntresses
p
Sì, è l'A-mor un cac-cia-
Ja, A-mor, das ver-schmitz-te
Yes, Cu-pid, with his ro-guish
cac-cia-tor, il suo stral sa lan-ciar; ma se im-pia-ga,
schmitz-te Kind, trug den Pfeil wie der Wind, A-mor trug den
ro-guish art, Like the wind bore the dart! Cu-pid with his
to-re, il suo stra-le sa lan-cia-re; ma se im-pia-ga, sa quel
Kind, es trug den Pfeil ge-schwind, ge-schwind, ja, A-mor trug den Pfeil ge-
art, now like the wind he bore the dart, ay, Cu-pid, with his ro-guish

più facile
Ah!
Ah!
sa quel duol al-leg-giar!
Pfeil ge-schwind wie der Wind!
art, his art, bore the dart!
duol, ah! al-leg-giar!
schwind, ge-schwind wie der Wind!
art, ah! bore the dart!
pp
Chorus
sa quel
ja, ge-
Like the
duol al- - leg- - giar!
schwind wie der Wind!
wind he bore it!
exeunt Huntresses
p
cresc.

2